From Medicine Man to Medical Doctor

The Medical History of Early Santa Clara Valley

Elizabeth Ahrens-kley
Gerald E. Trobough, MD
Michael A. Shea, MD

Almaden Press: A Stone Publishing Company

Acknowledgements

We would like to express our gratitude to the following people for contributing to the content and completion of this book. Pam Jensen,managing editor of *The Bulletin*, which is the bi-monthly journal of the Santa Clara County Medical Association. Tom Livingston and Marc Pinnell, our publisher and graphic designer, in that order. Marylou Lyon. one of the authors long time favorite history teacher. Mary Hanel, librarian at the Santa Clara Public Library. Lisa Christiansen, librarian at the Stocklmeir Library at DeAnza College. Bill Wulf, Los Gatos Historian, who furnished original material on Mountain Charley. Drew Bourn, history curator at the Lane Medical Library at Stanford University. Peggy Conaway, Los Gatos Librarian. Don Watters, Los Gatos Historian, and Deborah Oropeza, Mission Santa Clara Archivist at Santa Clara University Library. Last but not least, Marilyn Shea who provided the clue to the naming of the book, which was one of the largest hurdles that we encountered.

Dedication

This book is dedicated to all the pioneer physicians who followed their dreams West, practiced their crafts, established hospitals, and founded medical schools, thus securing the future of medicine in California.

Contents

INTRODUCTION

This potpourri of medical history of the Santa Clara Valley tells a story of medicine that took place during the early years.

It begins with the Ohlone Indians, a local tribe that lived in our valley for over five thousand years. Shaman(medicine man) and midwives were their primary practitioners. Botanical preparations (e.g. herbs) were their mainstay medicines. Other treatment regimens were splinting of fractures and trephining for seizures and severe headaches.

Following the Ohlone years came the Spanish, Mexican, and American periods. Medical practice was still in its infancy as evidenced by treatment routines such as bloodletting, purgatives, and poultices. Surgery was done initially without anesthesia and antiseptics and was generally unsatisfactory.

Pioneer physician biographies such as John Marsh, John Townsend, (the first American trained physician in California), Benjamin Cory (The first American resident physician in San Jose), Henry H. Warburton, Isaac Isbel, and others will be found in the book.

Well known medical facilities, such as Agnews State Hospital, San Jose Hospital, Santa Clara County Hospital, UCSF Medical School, and Stanford Medical School(including their founders Hugh Toland and Levi Cooper Lane respectively) are all explored.

Stories of pioneer women doctors, such as Euthanasia Meade (yes that is her real name) and Elizabeth Gallimore are all presented.

The chapter on gold rush medicine gives us a glimpse into the world of the buggy riding family doctor of the mid eighteen hundreds. What a challenge that must have been, without antibiotics, without safe and sterile surgery, without diagnostic tools such as blood work and x rays.

The book closes with the life story of a more contemporary and well known educator and physician, Leon P. Fox.

We hope our endeavor will bring to you a greater understanding of medicine's past, a deeper appreciation of its present, and an optimistic view into its future.

About the Authors

Beth Ahrens Kley, after growing up overseas (Japan and Thailand), graduating from the University of California Santa Cruz in 1977, and later living in Germany for ten years (Jena, Thuringia), she returned to Santa Cruz and took up research on family ancestry, including her maternal great, great grandfather, Dr. Benjamin Cory. In June 2001, she won first place in the California Pioneers of Santa Clara County historical essay contest. The title was "Dr. Benjamin Cory, Pioneer and First Medical Physician of San Jose, California." She remains fascinated by historical pastimes and is a member of the SCCMA history committee. Her mother, Carolyn Cory Ahrens, great granddaughter of Dr. Benjamin Cory, also presently resides in Santa Cruz, California.

Dr. Gerald E. Trobough is an actively practicing physician with Los Olivos Women's Medical Group in Los Gatos, California. He specializes in Infertility and Gynecology. As an avid student of medical history and history of the Western Frontier, he has written articles and lectured on these subjects. He is a member of the History Committee of the Santa Clara County Medical Association.

Michael A. Shea MD is a retired Obstetrician-Gynecologist, who has been researching California History over the past twenty years. He is currently a member of the Santa Clara County Medical Association's History Committee, and has written numerous articles on local medical history. He is also a member of the California Pioneers of Santa Clara County. In 2012, he was awarded first place in their annual historical essay contest. The paper was titled "Nineteenth Century Medicine in the Santa Clara Valley." He presently resides in Almaden, a suburb of San Jose, California.

Hippocrates

By Michael A. Shea, MD

Many of us remember the Hippocratic oath in medical school. What we may not recall is the story about Hippocrates, from whom much of the oath was derived.

Known as the father of medicine, Hippocrates was born in 460 B.C. on the island of Cos (Kos), in the southeastern Aegean Sea, about 200 miles southeast of Athens, Greece.

After receiving a good general education, he served an apprenticeship in medicine under his father, Herakleidas, and another physician, Herodikos. Shortly after, he left Cos for the land of the Thessalians, just north of Athens.

Hippocrates stressed observation and a scientific approach to the diagnosis and treatment of disease. He is credited with separating medicine from philosophy, mythology, and religion. Under his teachings, medicine became an independent science;

a body of knowledge unto itself. He proposed dietetics, exercise, cleanliness, and nutrition as the basis for prevention and treatment of illness. An idea that is espoused even today.

His dietary advice included honey and water, barley soup, pomegranate juice, plus a balanced diet of meat, fish, vegetables, and fruit.

He was also the first to suspect some diseases might be transported by air or water. He suspected epidemics to occur due to contaminated winds coming in contact with large masses of people.

The most famous work of medical writings for these times was the Hippocratic Corpus. It was a large volume of 70 works that described all aspects of medical and surgical disorders and their treatment. Most scholars attribute this collection to a number of physicians, including Hippocrates. The works contain the conservative approach to treatment, as well as more active methods. It is interesting to list some of the active treatments in the Corpus because they were still a significant part of medical practice into the middle of the nineteenth century.

1. Venesection or bloodletting (based on the four humor theory of blood, phlegm, yellow bile, and black bile).
2. Purgatives (emetics and laxatives for gastrointestinal disease).
3. Poultices (topical concoctions used to treat visible tumors).
4. Trephination (placing holes in the skull to treat such conditions as "water on the brain").
- Surgical procedures involving the kidney – the draining of abscesses or removal of stones.
5. Treatment of fractures and dislocations with splinting and manipulation.
6. Vasectomy – recorded as a surgical procedure for permanent birth control.

Some of Hippocrates other accomplishments include:

7. Treating the king of Macedonia, who was suffering from consumption.
8. Predicting the spread of epidemics based on wind patterns.
9. Founding a medical school in Cos in 400 B.C.
10. Being listed by Plato as the master of his art.
11. Although not the sole author, he contributed to one of history's most famous documents, the Hippocratic oath. This is printed below in its complete form.

THE OATH

I swear by Apollo the healer, by Aesculapius, by Health and all the powers of healing, and call to witness all the gods and goddesses that I may keep this oath and promise to the best of my ability and judgment.

I will pay the same respect to my master in the Science as to my parents and share my life with him and pay all my debts to him. I will regard his sons as my brothers and teach them the Science, if they desire to learn it, without fee or contract. I will hand on precepts, and all other learning to my sons, to those of my master, and to those pupils duly apprenticed and sworn, and to none other.

I will use my power to help the sick to the best of my ability and judgment; I will abstain from harming any man by it.

I will not give a fatal draught to anyone if I am asked, nor will I suggest any such thing. Neither will I give a woman means to procure an abortion.

I will be chaste and religious in my life and in my practice.

I will not cut, even for the stone, but I will leave such procedures to the practitioners of that craft.

Whenever I go into a house, I will go to help the sick and never with the intention of doing harm or injury. I will not abuse my position to indulge in sexual contacts with the bodies of women or of men, whether they be free men or slaves.

Whatever I see or hear, professionally or privately, which ought not to be divulged, I will keep secret and tell no one.

If, therefore, I observe this oath and do not violate it, may I prosper both in my life and in my profession, earning good repute among all men for all time. If I transgress and forswear this oath, may my lot be otherwise.

Hippocrates died in 377 B.C. He left behind two sons, Thessalos and Dracon, who apprenticed under their father and carried on his tradition.

The Valley's First Practitioner

By Michael A. Shea, MD

Before the Americans, before the Mexicans, before the Spanish, there were the Ohlones. This Indian tribe lived and flourished in our county for over 5,000 years.

The art of healing among the tribe evolved over time. By the 1800s, they could treat minor aches, pains, colds, and flu with a variety of herbal medicines. They knew how to set fractures, tamponade bleeding wounds with compresses of animal hair, and even induce abortion. For serious illnesses, there was a special healer called the shaman.

He or she (mostly male) received their calling at an early age. This was usually through a dream-type vision. Apprenticeship with the current shaman would then commence until the student was deemed ready to practice on his own. This would take several years. A shaman was held in high esteem by the tribe and was considered wealthy by Indian standards.

When a family member became seriously ill, the shaman was offered a fee of clam shell beads (Ohlone money) and, if accepted, the patient-healer relationship was established.

The Indian concept of disease was that it was caused by the victim's enemy (i.e., putting a hex on someone). It was the shaman's job to find the pain caused by an evil one and remove it.

Proper attire was important to the shaman and certainly impressed the fretting family. His face was painted black, and black stripes lined his wrists, shoulders, thighs, and ankles. He would wear a skirt of raven feathers and hold a wand of eagle feathers in his hand. Suspended from his belt was the foot of a coyote, while around his neck hung a string of bear claws and the head of a falcon. Tufts of feathers on weasel skin bracelets dangled from his wrists, while cocoon rattles jangled around his ankles. Chanting and dancing would then go on for hours. This was designed to call on help from the animal gods. These could be any of the following: coyote, eagle, hummingbird, falcon, lizard, or grizzly bear. These animal gods could be of real benefit to the shaman, especially if seen in a dreamlike state brought on by the repetitive dancing and chanting.

After hours, even days of this ritual, the final part of the treatment was begun. A medicine pouch of otter skin was produced. It contained a hollow bone tube, a small flint knife, coyote hair, fingernails, cougar whiskers, an inchworm, and other assorted objects. The shaman made a small superficial incision over the area of suspected disease and placed the hollow tube over the cut. He sucked hard and strong. Gagging and choking, he put his hand to his mouth and spat out the offending agent. It could be a ball of coyote hair or any of the other objects in the medicine pouch. If the shaman was lucky, the patient would awaken refreshed and cured. If he was unlucky, the patient would die. Crestfallen, he would return the beads to the family, in hopes they would not plot to harm him.

A colorful character, a magician, a spiritualist, a practitioner, could all describe the person who held this high ranking position among the local tribe. He was, above all, their shaman, and he practiced his art for thousands of years right here in our Bay Area.

An Ohlone Birth

By Michael A. Shea, MD

For over 3,000 years, the Ohlone Indians lived along the Califomia coast from the San Francisco Bay to Point Sur. In the early 1700s, there were 40 separate and distinct tribelets, each consisting of approximately 250 people for a total population of 10,000.

Under the ramada (shade hut), a young pregnant Ohlone woman is helping some of the older tribal women weave baskets for the fall acorn harvest. She is careful not to use an awl (a sharpened animal bone) in the work, as she has been told that it could cause her baby to be born blind. She is content to strip sedge roots with her teeth and let the others put the baskets together.

The pregnancy is growing long and she has done all the proper things. She has avoided meat, fish, and salt, in order to keep her weight down and lessen her chances of having a difficult labor that a large baby might cause. She has been polite to people, animals, and avoided looking into the night sky, lest she see an owl or a shooting star. All of these will help keep her baby healthy.

As she works, there is a subtle firmness in her abdomen. The abdominal skin is warm to the touch and a mild backache accompanies the contraction. It lasts about 60 seconds. She feels apprehensive, as she has not felt pain with her contractions in the past. The basket weavers also take notice, especially the one who is known as the thin woman. She is recognized by the tribe as an experienced midwife. The mother-to-be is comfortable around the thin woman and is relieved to know that she will be with her for her labor and delivery.

The pains occur more frequently and move from her back to her abdomen. They are stronger and she retires to her dwelling, where there is a small fire

burning. The thin woman stays with her, holding her gaze, and keeping her calm.

Posture in labor took many forms in the Native Americans. Partially squatting, the Sioux pulled on a leather strap attached to a vertical pole. The Blackfoot kneeled during labor, hands grasping an upright pole. Other tribes, across the West, used other positions: kneeling while pulling on a horizontal crossbar, squatting alone, or the dorsal lithotomy position. Some even applied tourniquet belt devices above the abdomen and tightened down with each contraction. Among the Nez Perce, the squaws would squat during the first stage of labor, but lie down for the actual delivery, usually on their side. We do not know how the Ohlone labored, but the latter method is the best guess.

Contractions are getting stronger, coming every five minutes, and the thought of some herbal medicine for pain comes to her mind. The Ohlones used Jimsonweed in tea form for the relief of pain. This herb contains atropine and scopolamine-like compounds which result in pain relief, sedation, and euphoria. Although it is tempting, she refuses the Jimsonweed for fear it will have an adverse effect on her baby.

The hours pass. Daylight is fading. There is some concern in her mind that she is not progressing satisfactorily. The contractions are regular and strong, but are they strong enough? The Native Americans had knowledge of a powerful oxytocic found in rattlesnake tail beads. They knew it could help a labor that was not strong enough. (Sacagawea had used it in her labor just before she joined the historic Lewis and Clark Expedition.)

The thin woman, sensing her fear, calmly reaches into her pouch and removes a bear claw, which she places on the young girl's abdomen. This is followed by even stronger contractions and a sudden uncontrollable urge to push.

"I see the head" shouts one of the older women, excitedly. The thin woman stretches the perineum as the baby's head emerges, followed quickly by a pink, squirming baby boy. Sighing deeply, the new mother feels the immediate relief of all the pressure and pain. The baby cries lustily and everyone smiles thankfully.

Hardly noticed by her is the small gush of blood followed by the delivery of the placenta. This is quickly passed to one of the attending women, who takes it outside, where it is burned and properly disposed of.

After a brief rest, mother and baby are led to a nearby stream, where clear cold water splashes on their skin. The baby wails, as if insulted, but to the mother, it is refreshing.

Meanwhile, her husband, who had not participated in the labor or delivery (this was the Indian custom), goes to the home where he digs a long pit and fills it with stones. He builds a fire on top of the stones. When the stones are warm, he rakes off the ashes and adds a deep layer of aromatic herbs and soft brush.

When mother and baby return, she sees the new bed and inhales the fragrant aroma. She embraces her husband, and then tenderly places her baby beside her on the soft warm mattress, where both fall into a deep restful sleep.

For several thousand years, this was the Ohlone way.

Trephination in History

By Michael A Shea, MD

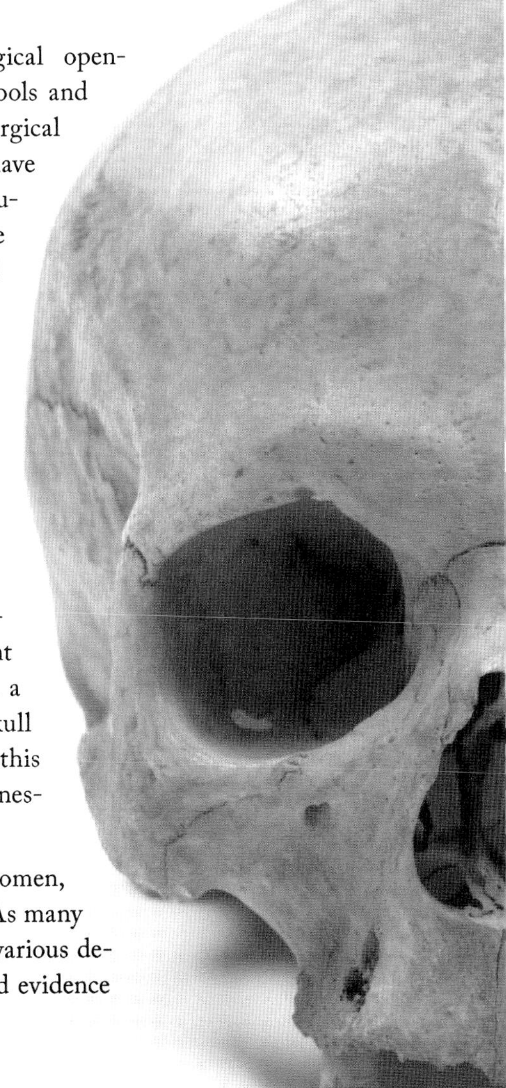

Primitive cranial trephining, the surgical opening of the skull performed with primitive tools and techniques, is one of the most interesting surgical practices in human history. It is thought to have originated in the Neolithic Period, seven thousand years ago. Hippocrates and Galen wrote about trephining and the practice continued throughout the Middle Ages and into the Renaissance.

Evidence has been found for this practice in Peru, Bolivia, Europe, Asia, New Zealand, and North America. The Ohlone Indians in our bay area also practiced trephining.

The operation consisted of removing a piece of skull (frontal, parietal, or occipital) from a living patient to expose the dura mater. If the dura remained intact, the patient in the pre-anesthesia, pre-antisepsis era had a fair chance of surviving the operation. The skull has relatively few sensory nerve fibers and this allowed trephining to be tolerated without anesthesia.

The procedure has been done on men, women, and children, with the majority being men. As many as two-thirds of the skulls examined reveal various degrees of new bone growth. This is considered evidence for survival. Considering the danger of severe bleeding, brain damage, and infection, survival of two-thirds of subjects suggest considerable skill and experience of the operator.

Why It Was Done

The motives for ancient trephining have been the subject of speculation since the discovery of the first specimens in the nineteenth century. Possible reasons include all of the following: to allow for the escape of evil spirits, headaches, fractures, infections, or convulsions. Another suggestion has been to acquire rondelles (discs of bone) which were used as charms or amulets.

Technique

There were three general techniques: scraping, drilling, and cutting.

The earliest skulls from the Stone Age were done long before metallurgy. The holes were made with a sharp-edge flint or knife. The practioner would go deeper and deeper until the dura was exposed. A circular or rectangular opening was the result. Some healing of new bone would occur, but unless the opening was only one centimeter or less, the hole would remain open. They would cover the wound with a shell, gourd, or even a piece of silver.

The bow drill was one of the more common methods used for trephining. It was made of a wood drill with an obsidian tip and a leather thong wrapped around it several times. The operator would place the drill tip on the head and pull the leather thong. There are some skulls that have up to five holes present.

Neurosurgery, a relatively modern specialty, seems to have its roots in an operation done seven thousand years ago.

Bloodletting

By Michael A. Shea, MD

The practice of bloodletting dates back several thousand years. It was extremely popular in America in the nineteenth century. Two theories for the etiology of disease were responsible for its use: (1) There was an imbalance in one of the four humors (blood, phlegm, black bile, and yellow bile); (2) The circulatory system was in a state of excitability and needed to be relaxed.

Benjamin Rush, MD, was the most influential proponent of bloodletting in the United States. He recommended it for treatment of convulsions, concussion, labor pain, hernia, smallpox, croup, pneumonia, and any other disease that produced a fever.

The method used in bloodletting was straightforward. With the patient sitting upright, a tourniquet was applied to the upper arm. A single blade lancet or a multiple blade lancet (scarificator) was used to cut the vein in the arm. A cup, usually made of glass, was heated and applied to the bleeding site. This added a small amount of suction to the procedure. The blood was collected in a volume marked bleeding bowl until the desired amount was obtained or the patient fainted. The process was often repeated several times over several days until the patient started to recover or died. It is thought that George Washington's death was more directly related to bloodletting than to his respiratory infection.

The following is a vivid firsthand account of bloodletting in the nineteenth century:

The patient is the first wife of Salmon P. Chase, the future secretary of the treasury under Abraham Lincoln. The diagnosis was puerperal fever two weeks after delivery. The year was 1837.

"The next morning (she had already been bled three times the previous day), such was her condition, there was a fair prospect of her recovery. All the symptoms boded well. But Drs. Drake and Richards were of the opinion that she had not been bled sufficiently, and that the disease had not been subdued. They, accordingly, recommended further bleeding; Dr. Colby opposed it, saying that all her symptoms were improved, and they ought to watch the result. The other physicians insisted, however. It was anticipated that the effect would be to reduce the frequency of the pulse and augment its volume. Kitty was told that the doctors thought of bleeding her again, and was asked if she was willing. She said "Yes, anything." She was then raised up in bed and twenty ounces of blood were taken from her. The physicians seemed to entertain some hopes of her recovery, and agreed upon a course of treatment to be adopted. The (patient's) father came into her room exclaiming, 'Thank God, my child, the doctors say there is hope.' She said nothing. All hope had vanished. Dr. Drake felt her pulse, and said she was dead."

Bloodletting retained its popularity until the latter half of the nineteenth century. Bacteriology, the germ theory, and the growing realization that bloodletting was detrimental to the patient, finally put its use to rest.

Medical Care at Mission Santa Clara

By Gerald E. Trobough, MD

Mission Santa Clara de Asis was established in 1777 by Spanish Franciscan Priests in the Santa Clara Valley. The goal of the Franciscans was to convert the Ohlone Indians to Christianity and teach them skills to make them productive citizens. The women were taught cooking and sewing skills and the men learned how to farm wheat, com, and beans, and how to raise and tend cattle and sheep.

The original plan of the missionaries was to secularize the land surrounding the Mission within 1 0 years. The goal was to distribute land to the well trained Ohlone Indians to farm and establish ranches. However, secularization was delayed in most of the California Missions. The missionaries did not feel the Indians were ready for a life outside of the regimentation of mission life. Mission Santa Clara was not secularized until 60 years later in 1837.

Mission Santa Clara was regarded as one of the cleanest and best regulated of all the Missions. It had the highest number of baptisms and marriages but it also had the highest numbers of deaths and burials. The reasons indicated for the high mortality rates at Santa Clara were inconclusive.

Life at the Mission had a disastrous effect on the health of the Ohlones. The Europeans brought new and contagious diseases to the area including measles, mumps, small pox, and influenza. Since the Ohlones had no prior exposure or immunity to these diseases, and were living in overcrowded conditions, the infections spread rapidly killing many people. They suffered through one epidemic after another. A study done in 1806 documented that one-third of the children under age 5 who contracted measles died. One of the worst killers was syphilis which affected many native Indians. Most blamed the Spaniards for introducing syphilis to California, however, some believed it was endemic in the Indian tribes. Medical care for syphilis was poor and ineffective. The use of Mercury pills to treat the symptoms was often worse than the disease.

Poor quality health care also played a role in high infant mortality and the high death rates in women of childbearing age. Pregnant women did not receive adequate pre-natal care from the Franciscans. The priests would not allow the use of midwives, who specialized in caring for women and young children, to help when there were problems. Many babies were born with low birth weights and had chronic ailments, including congenital syphilis, and did not live long. Seventy-five percent of the babies born to parents with syphilis died before the age of one due to the ravages of congenital syphilis. Poor sanitation and polluted water in the Mission resulted in diarrhea and a myriad of infections which lead to a high mortality rate among children.

Little is written about the medical care at the Missions. It is known that every Mission had its own "hospital" that consisted of a room with a mat on the floor rather than a bed. The Padres had medical and surgical kits and they were instructed on basic medical and surgical care. There were no full-time physicians on staff at the Missions. Medical assistance came from the Presidio of Monterey where the Surgeon-Generals of the Spanish Army resided. Dr. Jose Davila, the third Surgeon-General, helped to establish medical care at Mission Dolores in San Francisco in 1777 and at the Mission Santa Clara in 1778.

Dr. Pablo Solar was the 5th Surgeon-General, from 1791-1800. A native of Barcelona, he was considered the best and most skillful surgeon to come from the Monterey Presidio. He established primitive medical guidelines for the Missions. Father Jose Viader came to the Santa Clara Mission in 1796 to assist Father Magin Catala in operating the Mission. Father Viator wrote a reference book on the Mission in 1798 (This book is housed at Santa Clara University Library in the Archives and Special Collection Section). The book has three references to medical care that were attributed to Dr. Solar. The first reference is to the instruction given to the Padres on vaccinating against small pox. This reference was documented several years before Dr. Edward Jenner published his series on vaccination using cow pox. It is unknown how many vaccinations were done at Mission Santa Clara and their impact on mortality rates.

The second reference of Viater's book gave instructions on doing a Caesarian Section. It was very detailed on technique. It was only allowed to be done when the mother died (post-mortem) in an effort to save and baptize the child. At least one C-Section was done at Mission Santa Clara. The third reference was related to herbal treatments of symptoms or disease. These treatments included:

- Kidney Disease – Sweet Almond Oil
- Colic – Chamomile
- Scurvy – Extract of Juniper

- Wound Healing – Camphor
- Insomnia – Milk of Almonds
- Indigestion – Gentile Balm
- Cough – Flower of Violets
- Erysipelas – Tea of elderberry
- Laxative – Tea of Senna
- Diarrhea – Plantain
- Dropsy – Powder of root of Julep
- Scrofula – Pomade of frogs
- Poison – Licorice roots and sarsaparilla
- Fractures – Poultice of frogs and quicksilver

There were many other herbs that were apparently listed in their pharmacy. Unfortunately, the primitive treatment of diseases by the Mission priests was ineffective. The padres' lack of medical knowledge and their belief that diseases and epidemics were a punishment by God, created distrust among the Ohlones. In times of medical need, the missionaries did not allow the Indians to seek the help of their tribal Shamans. As a result, many of the Ohlone converts held secret meetings and performed dance ceremonies to their traditional spirits hoping for a cure. Some of the Indians ran away from the Mission and back to their elders looking for a Shaman who would chant, suck blood and perform other familiar healing practices. The Padres' medicine had failed them. They believed their tribal spirits would intercede.

Gold Rush Medicine

By Michael A. Shea, MD

1849 saw the greatest migration of native and foreign pioneers in California history. The non-Indian population grew from 15,000 to over 100,000 in one year. By the end of 1852, it had reached 224,435.

Adventure and gold were the motivators for this growth, and doctors were not

immune. Hundreds of doctors made the trek during the first few years. Most came for gold, but soon gave up the pan for the practice of medicine.

There was more than enough medical work to be done. Diseases, such as malaria, scurvy, typhoid, erysipelas, smallpox, tuberculosis, cholera, and dysentery were found throughout California. Trauma was, however, the largest component of medical practice. Amputation, bone setting, and wound treatment were everyday challenges for the local "doc." Unfortunately, he had minimal training or experience in these areas.

Most physicians of this time were trained in preceptorships. They would pay a fee and work for the doctor for one to two years. If the doctor was a good teacher, they received good training. If he was not, they suffered for it. Medical schools, at this time, were available to some of these students, but for only four-month periods, each year, for two years.

There were three methods of practice in America at this time—Allopaths (regulars), Homeopaths, and Eclectics. Allopaths were in the majority and followed the teachings of Dr. Benjamin Rush, a nationally-recognized leader. He taught that all diseases could be treated by a combination of (1) bloodletting and (2) purging (laxatives and emetics), and (3) poultices (a warming compound applied to the skin).

Listed below are some of the common medicines found in Dr. Benjamin Cory's diary, which he had kept on his 1847 journey overland. He was the first physician to live and practice in San Jose.

- Calomel tablets (mercurous chloride) - used to induce copious diarrhea.
- Laudanum drops - an alcoholic preparation from the opium poppy (similar to morphine).
- Tartar Emetic (potassium antimony nitrate) - used to induce vomiting and as an expectorant.
- Potassium Iodide - used to thin secretions.
- Oil of Cloves - used as a topical analgesic for toothaches.
- Camphor - from the bark of the Camphor tree. Used topically to relieve pain and itching of the skin.
- Blue Mass Pills - contained mercury salts. Used to treat a variety of diseases including depression. Abraham Lincoln used this drug for his mood disorder, but discontinued them because they caused irritability.
- Asafoetida (stinking gum) - found in the root of an herb, ferula. It actually had some anti-microbial properties and was used in bronchitis patients.
- Corton Oil - from the seeds of a small tree native to India. Used topically to cause burning and redness of the skin (poulticing).

Although not in Dr. Cory's diary, quinine was a very popular treatment for fevers of any etiology.

Doctors of the day made a very decent living. Income from medical practice was $75.00 - $100.00 per day. Office visits were two ounces of gold dust ($32.00 dollars). Laudanum charges were one dollar per drop and quinine one dollar a grain. These prices were not out of line as boots sold for $40.00 a pair, potatoes, a dollar a pound, and a haircut was five dollars.

Surgery in 1849 was in its infancy. Anesthesia was either whiskey or laudanum, with or without restraints. Morbidity and mortality rates were unacceptably high. Most surgeons were restricted to setting fractures, draining abcesses, and performing amputations. It would be a few years before anesthesia (ether and chloroform) and aseptic technique would lower morbidity and mortality rates and allow general surgical procedures to become more commonplace.

The gold rush physician relied on his savvy and his senses, plus an array of chemicals and botanicals to bring relief to the suffering. He gave it his best with what he had to work with.

John Marsh

The First American Practitioner in California

By Michael A. Shea, MD

Preface: The following is a quote from an old wizened woman to author George Lyman in 1930. "Over there," said she, "in an adobe at the base of that mountain, lived the most mysterious of California's pioneers. His name was John Marsh. He was a doctor, a hermit, a misanthrope. He hated men."

John Marsh

John Marsh, a descendant of the first minister of the first Christian Church in Massachusetts, was born in 1799 in Danver, Massachusetts. He was the eldest of seven siblings. Showing no love for farm life, he enrolled in a boarding school, Lancaster Academy, where his curriculum was classical studies, including Latin and Greek. Answering a call to the ministry, he changed schools and attended Phillips Academy. Graduating in 1819, he then enrolled at Harvard to further pursue his religious avocation. Dismissed in his second year for participating in a student rebellion, he was allowed to return one year

The Stone House

later as a junior. At this time, he changed his major to premed. During his senior year he took gross anatomy and spent some time under the tutelage of Dr. John Dixwell, of Boston. He graduated from Harvard in 1823 with a Bachelor of Arts degree.

Needing money to go on to Harvard Medical School, he accepted a two-year obligation, teaching military dependents at Fort St. Anthony, on the Mississippi River in Michigan territory. It was here that he also studied under the post surgeon, Dr. Edward Purcell. Due to Dr. Purcell's sudden death, he received no written confirmation of his preceptorship. While teaching at the Fort, he fell in love with a part-French, part-Sioux woman, named Marguerite Deconteaux. Although not married, they had a son, Charles, in 1825. Deciding not to return to Harvard for medical school, he stayed on at the Fort, where he was appointed Indian sub-agent. Several years later, Marguerite and their second baby died shortly after childbirth. This adverse event was followed by an indictment against John Marsh for selling guns to the Indians. He planned to escape his legal problem by moving west. For reasons unclear, he left his six-year-old son with a faith healer in Salem, Massachusetts, promising to return for him in a few years. This was not to be.

In 1832, the pioneer was found operating a general store in Independence, Missouri. The business failed and he was off to Santa Fe, New Mexico, just ahead of his creditors. From here, it was on to the Pueblo of Los Angeles, in California. He arrived in 1836, penniless, and finding no doctors in the area, presented his Harvard diploma to the City Council under the guise of a medical degree. As it was written in Latin, the council referred it to the Franciscan padres at San Gabriel Mission, where they unexplainably confirmed it as a medical diploma. He was, from that time on, known as Doctor John Marsh. He practiced in L.A. with very few treatment options. He had brandy and quinine for fevers, aches, and pains, and some cowpox vaccine that he used to immunize patients against smallpox. He developed quite a following for attending childbirth, although there is no known record of any training in this field. Cowhides, worth two dollars each, were the main method of payment in those times.

Selling his practice to a Boston trader for $500 dollars, he moved north to the San Jose area. There he purchased a 7,000 acre ranch, Los Meganos, 40 miles north of San Jose, at the foot of Mount Diablo. He financed his large cattle and horse ranch by practicing medicine. He was known to travel miles to see patients, but was also known for his expensive fees. He developed a reputation for rudeness and being inhospitable. This ran against the grain of most of his neighboring Californios.

Desiring security in a Mexican-run California, he wrote letters to people in Missouri, extolling the virtues of California and encouraging them to move west. Some did make the long journey, as a result of John Marsh's letters, including the first pioneer wagon train of the Bartleson Bidwell Party in 1841.

In 1850, he married Abigail Smith Tuck (Abby), a devout Baptist school teacher. They had a daughter, Alice, two years later. In 1855, Abby passed away from what probably was tuberculosis.

There were two California bright spots in the life of John Marsh. One was the large stone house that he built near his adobe home. It was considered by many to be the finest example of old English architecture in the state. The second was the surprise return of his son, Charles, in 1856. It was an emotional reunion and seemed to soften the heart of father Marsh.

The sudden ending of John Marsh's life came one day in 1856, when he was stabbed multiple times by one of his vaqueros while enroute to San Francisco. The reason was a dispute over wages paid to the worker after branding the Marsh cattle. Ten years later, son Charles found the culprit, Felipe Morena, and after a trial, he was sentenced to life in San Quentin. However, 25 years later, Governor Markham pardoned Morena.

The extensive estate of John Marsh gradually eroded away, as squatters and towns encroached upon the land. The stone house, however, remains, and is being restored at this time.

John Marsh was an enigmatic man. Wherever he went, there was action and adventure. He was broke. He was rich. He was good. He was bad. He was loved. He was hated. Although his medical training was borderline, he was the first American to practice in California. For this alone, John Marsh will always be remembered, and like the beacon atop Mt. Diablo, his memory will endure.

John Townsend, MD

Pioneer Doctor

By Michael A. Shea, MD

John Townsend

John Townsend was born circa 1810 in Fayette County, Pennsylvania. Two years after earning his M.D. degree from Lexington College, he began an odyssey that took him through Ohio, Indiana, and Missouri.

In 1832, while practicing medicine in Ohio, he placed a ring on the finger of Elizabeth Louise Schallenberger. Wanderlust called again, in 1844, when the Missouri couple joined the Stephens Party, bound for a relatively unsettled California. This courageous group of pioneers were the first to cross the Sierra Nevada range with wagons. They accomplished this by way of the Donner-Truckee route, shown to them by an indian named Truckee.

Arriving at Sutter's Fort, near present-day Sacramento, Dr. Townsend joined Captain Sutters' forces, in support of Governor Micheltorena, in one of California's civil wars. He served as surgeon and aide de camp to the group. After this brief and bloodless crusade, he began his practice at Sutter's Fort.

1847 found the Townsend couple in Monterey, only to move shortly to Yerba Buena (renamed that same year to San Francisco, in honor of Saint Francis of Assisi, founder of the Franciscan missionaries who established all of California's 21 missions). His office and residence was located on the south side of California street, between Montgomery and Sansome.

Political talent surfaced as he was elected alcalde (mayor) of San Francisco, plus was a member of the town council (ayuntamiento). He also served on the first school board and helped establish the first schoolhouse in San Francisco.

He had an interest in real estate, as evidenced by his partnership with a Belgian named, Corneille de Boon. Together, they developed a large project in the Hunter's Point area. It, however, did not succeed. One project that did succeed was the birth of his only child, a son named John Henry Townsend.

In commemoration of his many public services, one of San Francisco's important thoroughfares, Townsend Street, bears his name.

Tiring of the fast-paced San Francisco scene, he purchased 195 acres, north of San Jose, on what is now the Old Oakland Road. He also acquired an adobe home nearby. In addition to practicing medicine, he developed his acreage into a prosperous orchard. For years, this area was known as Townsend Corners.

He devoted much energy to keeping the capital of California in San Jose, even offering a sizable gift of land for this purpose. In July 1850, he helped to organize San Jose Lodge No. 10 F. and A.M., the first Masonic Lodge between San Francisco and the Mexican border.

It was at this time that the cholera epidemic found its way to the Santa Clara Valley. Dr. Townsend worked diligently to save others but on December 8, 1850, he, himself, died from the disease. One month later, Mrs. Townsend succumbed to the same illness.

John Henry Townsend, orphaned at two years of age, was raised by his uncle, Moses Schallenberger, who lived nearby. John eventually earned a law degree from Cambridge University, and returned to San Jose with his English wife to work and manage the orchard property. He served in the state assembly in 1883 and 1884, was a county supervisor, and also became director of the Santa Clara Valley Agricultural Society. He died in 1941 (age ninety-three).

Doctor John Townsend was a man of many vocations: overland immigrant, soldier of fortune, physician, politician, real estate promoter, and rancher. He also has the distinction of being the first American-trained physician to settle and practice medicine in California.

Benjamin Cory And Other Pioneer Physicians

Part 1

By Gerald E. Trobough, MD

Most historians agree that Dr. Benjamin Cory was the first American physician to settle in San Jose arriving on December 1, 1847. However, he may not have been the first American to treat San Jose residents. That distinction may belong to Dr. Isaac Isbell.

Isaac Chauncey Isbell (1800-1886)

Dr. Isbell, a medical graduate of the Western Reserve College in Ohio, decided to abandon his Chicago medical practice and move West to help settle the Wild Frontier. He sought advice and direction from Jacob and George Donner. The Donners made arrangements for Isbell and his wife to join the Aram-Imus wagon train originating in Springfield, Illinois. The Isbells purchased a wagon, team and supplies and left Illinois with thirty-one other wagons on April 14, 1846.

On the way west, the wagon train decided to take a safer approach crossing the Sierra Nevada Mountains than the Donner party. When they reached the Humboldt River their guide deserted them. Chief Truckee, head of the Paiute Tribe in Western

Nevada, agreed to guide them over the treacherous mountain terrain. It took their wagon sixteen days to cross the range and settle on the other side. They were fortunate that none of the wagons nor lives were lost in the process.

The Aram-Imus party encountered members of Colonel John Fremont' s battalion on the trail near Bear Valley. The soldiers led the Isbells to Fort Sutter where Isaac worked as a surgeon under Fremont's command. Fremont urged the party to go quickly to Mission Santa Clara to help fortify the Mission. War with Mexico had just started. The Aram-Imus party had fifty seven men and twelve to fifteen wagons. Upon arriving at the Mission in October of 1846, they surrounded the grounds. Approximately one hundred and seventy five Americans had been barricaded inside the mission walls awaiting an attack. However, the Mexicans did not attack but tried to keep them isolated and starving. Because of the women and children, Ignacio Alviso, the mayor of San Jose, gave the Americans wheat which kept them from starvation and death.

Fighting began in January of 1847 and was called The Battle of Santa Clara. It was reported that the Isbells watched the battle from a roof top at the Mission and the American commander used Mrs. Isbell wedding handkerchief for a white flag of truce. The fighting, however, ended in a draw with neither side the winning force. Mexico eventually surrendered and peace came to the area.

During the siege, Dr. Isbell contracted typhoid pneumonia. Many of the soldiers also developed typhoid fever in their damp and crowded quarters. Despite the number of soldiers who were ill and the many deaths at the mission, Dr. Isbell improved and directed his wife in the treatment of the soldiers who were sick. She distributed in excess of one hundred doses of medication in a day. Upon Dr. Isbell's recovery and the end of the war, he is said to have traveled to San Jose and administered medical services to those who came to the Pueblo. He had to swim his horse across the swollen Guadalupe River because of record rainfall that winter. However, there are some reports suggesting that he did not go to San Jose.

More famous, however, was Olive Mann Isbell, the doctor's wife. Olive was the niece of Horace Mann, the renowned educator in America. During the siege of the mission, Olive noted the tension and fear in the children and decided to start a school at the mission. A dilapidated stable, fifteen feet square with a hole in the roof, was converted to a school room. This was the first school in Santa Clara County and perhaps all of California. Having no text books, blackboard, chalk, pencils or paper, Olive drew her lessons in the dirt with a stick. The students used charcoal to write their ABC's on the palms of their hands. She had twenty five students and the school term was two months long.

In March of 1847, the Isbells moved to Monterey. Dr. Isbell set up a medical practice and Olive was encouraged by the United States Council to establish the first school in Monterey. The school was located above the jail. Olive had access to supplies for her students including some text books. She was guaranteed a salary of $200 for a three-month term. There were twenty four students, only two who spoke English.

The Isbells relocated to a cattle farm eight miles north of Stockton. When gold was discovered at Sutter's Mill, Dr. Isbell organized the Stockton Mining Company and set out for the gold fields. He also formed a trading post at the Weaverville Diggings. He made a considerable fortune estimated to be two million dollars. When he retired from mining, Dr. and Mrs. Isbell bought a ranch in Santa Paula located in Southern California. In 1926, a middle school was built in Santa Paula and named in Olive's honor. Dr. Isbell died in 1886 at the age of 86.

The Cory Brothers Modernized Medicine in Santa Clara County

By Elizabeth Ahrens-Kley

Dr. A. Jack Cory

Dr. Benjamin Cory

Arriving in San Jose in December of 1847, Dr. Benjamin Cory was the first American-trained physician to hang his shingle in the pueblo. Ben's tales of mining for gold, being an effective California state legislator, and the fight for improved sanitation and health service for the poor were enough to provide the necessary encouragement for his younger brother, Dr. Andrew Jackson (Jack) Cory, to also leave Ohio to join forces with his brother in the field of medicine in Santa Clara County. Between these two physicians, health care in San Jose was forever changed.

Both received their medical degrees from the Medical College of Ohio in Cincinnati, Ben in 1845 and Jack in 1860. Ben practiced alongside his father, Dr. J. M. Cory, in Ohio, for two years before crossing the plains by foot and oxen; Jack, upon receiving his medical degree, promptly sailed from the city of New York to San Francisco, and came directly to San Jose. In those crucial early years, these two brother physicians made their mark on medicine.

The new Santa Clara County Infirmary (Bascom Avenue is in the foreground)

THE HOSPITAL ON BASCOM AVENUE

In the first half of the 1850s, as a member of the San Jose Common Council, Dr. Ben Cory helped to lay the basic groundwork for care of the indigent sick in Santa Clara County. In these early years, sanitation was a serious problem. Epidemics of cholera, small pox, diphtheria, and other infectious diseases would strike regularly. There was no hospital; medicines and medical supplies were difficult to obtain. The doctor worked on sanitation ordinances and campaigned tirelessly for improvement in the city's health services. He surely was ecstatic to learn of Jack's interest in medicine, and his willingness to come to California to help in the vital struggle for better health care.

In 1860, the county hospital was relocated to South Street, west of Los Gatos Creek, but the city was growing rapidly, and the citizens objected to the "pest house" being in such close proximity. It again became necessary to move the hospital to a new location. Through the concerted efforts and leadership of Drs. Ben and Jack Cory, the county was able to purchase property for a hospital on Bascom Avenue, in 1871, and construction of the new Santa Clara County Infirmary (presently Santa Clara Valley Medical Center) was completed in 1875. Full operations began the next year, with six wards to accommodate 65 patients. Dr. Jack Cory was the first physician director of the hospital. He remained in charge of the county hospital for 11 years (1865-1876) and was the county coroner for a total of nine years. Dr. Ben Cory was the medical director of the hospital from 1880-1882.

CIVIC LEADERSHIP

By the death of Dr. Benjamin Cory in 1896, he had been practicing medicine in San Jose for nearly 50 years, longer than any other physician on the Pacific Coast, up until that time. Dr. Benjamin Cory and his brother, Dr. A. J. Cory, were motivated civic leaders, inspired by notions of public service to fellow citizens, the community, and the state. Through their combined efforts and effective leadership, the foundations for modern medicine were solidly planted in Santa Clara County.

Pioneer Physician of Santa Clara Township

Dr. Henry H. Warburton (1819-1903)

By Gerald E. Trobough, MD

The first physician to establish a practice in Santa Clara Township was Dr. Henry Hulme Warburton. Born in Staffordshire, England in 1819, Dr. Warburton received his medical training in England. He was part of a medical family as his father and six brothers were all physicians. For seven years he practiced with his father before coming to America in 1844. He practiced medicine in New York City for one year before moving to New London,

Connecticut to become a surgeon on board a whaling ship (The Corea) from 1845 to 1847. In 1847, he landed in Yerba Buena (San Francisco) and set up practice in Woodside for one year before moving to Santa Clara in 1848. He bought a home near the Santa Clara Mission.

During the Gold Rush, Dr. Warburton worked the mines for seven months. Upon his return to Santa Clara he purchased three hundred and twenty acres of farm land. In 1855, he married Catherine Pennell of San Francisco. They had seven children; two of whom died in childhood.

During the cholera epidemic of 1850, Dr. Warburton and a Mission physician, Dr. Espinosa, treated many patients. Dr. Espinosa contracted cholera and was successfully treated by Dr. Warburton. As the story goes, Dr. Warburton consumed a lot of brandy during the epidemic which prevented him from developing cholera.

In the 1850's, Dr. Warburton reputation earned him a large practice that included the Washington and Oregon territories. One time when riding his horse south of San Jose he wandered into the hideout of a bandit named Joaquin Murietta. The surprised Murietta was about to shoot Dr. Warburton when one of the bandit's lieutenants recognized the doctor as the man who had saved his child from diphtheria. Murietta agreed to spare Dr. Warburton if he promised not to divulge the hideout location. The doctor happily agreed.

Dr. Warburton attended to the Vasquez Family in Santa Clara numerous times. When the notorious bandit Tiburcio Vasquez was shot and captured in Southern California in 1874, he was brought back to San Jose and was hanged. The Vasquez Family pleaded with Dr. Warburton to treat the bandit's broken neck in an effort to save his life.

On a trip back to England in 1870, Dr. Warburton convinced one of his brothers and other relatives to move to California. James P. Warburton M.D. arrived and established a practice in San Francisco and Alameda.

The Warburtons built an office and home at 716 Main in Santa Clara in1886. The first floor was his office and the first pharmacy in town; the second floor was their residence. In 1966 his office was relocated to History Park in San Jose.

In February, 1903, while rushing back to his office from a house call, Dr. Henry Warburton collapsed and died at age 83. He had practiced in the area for fifty six years, the longest of any physician on the West Coast. In Dr. Warburton's honor, a street was named in his memory. The Santa Clara Civic Center is currently located on Warburton Avenue.

Benjamin Cory and Other Pioneer Physicians

Part 2

By Gerald E. Trobough, MD

Two San Jose pioneer physicians were notables during Ben Cory's time. They were Dr. Louis Hazelton Bascom and Dr. Alexander Josephus Spencer. Both physicians became partners ofDr. Cory.

Dr. Louis Bascom (1811-1881)

Dr. Louis and Mrs. Clara Bascom came to California in 1849 with two mule teams from Kentucky. They settled in San Jose and built two houses on the south side of San Fernando Street between First and Second Streets. They lived in one and the other became a boarding house." Slap Jack Hall" as the boarding house was known, was called that due to Mrs. Bascom's delicious pancakes.

Dr. Bascom was Dr. Cory's first partner. Both doctors were very busy during the cholera epidemic of 1850. They admitted the sickest cholera patients to the "Pest House" (later called City Hospital) which was located on Sixth Street. It was a large building located outside the walls of the Pueblo. Uninfected people had to be careful of their complaints because even a headache could land one in the Pest House.

Cory and Bascom provided all medications and took care of patients in the Pest house from November 7 to December 25, 1850. When they submitted their bill to the Committee Council (City Council) for $2472 for their expenses, the Council discounted their fee by $472 and only approved $2000 in February, 1853. The bill was finally certified correct in July, 1853 nearly one and a half years later. Payment of the bill occurred in August, 1853 with depreciated State Warrants that were worth much less than face value. (Was this the earliest form of managed care in the United States?)

Dr.'s Cory and Bascom continued their partnership until 1852. Dr. Bascom retired from medical practice and purchased 135 acres on the southern edge of Santa Clara and became a farmer. He named his home Somerville Lodge. In 1864, the road between San Jose and Los Gatos was named Bascom Avenue in his honor.

Perhaps more famous than her husband, was Clara Bascom. She preferred to be called Grandma and was a real character. When they arrived in San Jose they were short of money and his practice was slow. "Doc", Grandma said, "I'm going to do something to help!" Bascom laughed and said, "you can't do anything but talk." Grandma insisted she could make slap jacks and sell them. Doc was older than his wife and he loved her enthusiasm.

One day he came home and found a sign nailed to the side of the house that said "Slap Jack Hall". No sooner had the sign been hung, she was serving customers. She made slap jacks and served them with syrup and a cup of coffee for a dollar. Her place became famous. Clara had her piano shipped from Kentucky which was the first in San Jose. Her daughter entertained the crowd at Slapjack Hall with beautiful music.

San Jose became the first capitol of California and the first legislature convened in December, 1849. A number of the legislators would frequent Grandma's place and stay in the boarding house. Word spread throughout the mines about Grandma's cooking and the miners made sure to stop by for some famous pancakes when they came to town. They were always entranced by her constant chatter. Before the year was over Grandma had more money than Doctor Bascom.

When the State Capitol moved to Vallejo, Slap Jack Hall closed. Grandma, however, continued to entertain with her laughter and talking. With her talent for talking she raised money for charity and the South Methodist Church. People would say, "we'll pay you five dollars if you'll stop talking for five minutes!" Others paid her to talk as she was a good story teller. Grandma never saw anything but the amusing side of life. No one had ever heard her speak ill of anyone or express unhappiness even when her son and husband died. Grandma Bascom died in 1894 at the age of 78.

Benjamin Cory and Other Pioneer Physicians

Part 3

By Gerald E. Trobough, MD

Dr. Alexander Josephus Spencer (1806-1882)

Dr. A.J. Spencer was Dr. Cory's second partner. Spencer graduated at the top of his medical school class at Jefferson Medical College in Philadelphia. After several years of medical practice in the eastern part of the United States, he made his way to California during the Gold Rush of 1849. Due to an illness, he contracted at the mines, he moved back to Illinois but found it hard to forget about California. In 1852, he moved his family back to California and settled in San Jose. His wife was Miss Wright whose father was the governor of New York and the cousin of John Quincy Adams.

Spencer was the first surgeon of note to practice in Santa Clara County. He brought with him his surgical instruments that had been used by a British surgeon in the War of 1812. He was delighted with his San Jose practice. At that time, San Jose was a violent community with a multitude of shootings and accidents. While practicing in Illinois, he was used to getting paid 50 cents for an office visit. In San Jose he could charge $5.00, $10.00 or even $50.00 per visit. If surgery was required he often set his fee at a $1,000.

When Dr. Spencer became Dr. Cory's partner, they made the decision to buy a house together. They bought an old frame house and moved it to Second Street. Once settled, they partitioned the house into separate units. The Cory family lived in the South end and the Spencer family lived in the North end of the house. The families lived there for several years before realizing that their home had been used as the "Pest House" during the cholera epidemic of 1850.

While living in the duplex, the families had a problem with their horses being stolen. Dr. Cory had three horses stolen in one week. Dr. Spencer padlocked his horse to a redwood pole that was sunk into the ground. They devised an alarm system that would ring a bell in Frank Spencer's (oldest son) bed room if the stable door was opened. If the bell rang, Frank would go outside with a shotgun. This put an end to the horse stealing.

One of the most famous and often repeated story of Dr. Spencer was when he saved Mountain Charley's life. (See full story in previous issue of The Bulletin.) Charley had been mauled by a grizzly in 1854 and had a large portion of his scalp removed along with a skull fracture. A poorly done surgery had been performed by Dr. Thomas Ingersoll. Charley suffered severe headaches for a year before Dr. Spencer re-operated and put a silver plate in the scalp defect to cover the brain tissue. Spencer created the plate by pounding out a Spanish silver dollar. Charley lived that way for another forty eight years.

Another success story about Dr. Spencer, concerned a Spaniard who had been shot in the leg and was dying. The accident occurred in the Pinoche Mines one hundred miles south of San Jose. Dr. Spencer was summoned and relays of horses met the doctor in Gilroy and San Juan Bautista. He rode as swiftly as the horses would carry him. When he arrived the man was still breathing having been kept alive by a priest who sat at his bedside pressing the femoral artery for fifteen hours. When Dr. Spencer arrived the priest fainted from exhaustion. The Spaniard survived the surgery.

Dr. Spencer was staunchly opposed to the vigilantism and capital punishment of the era.. He often wrote articles condemning the vigilantes. This raised the ire of the group and the vigilantes made plans to hang the good doctor. One night as he was traveling to Gilroy the group planned to ambush him at the Twenty Mile House. Fortunately, his horse wandered off the trail while Spencer was dozing in the saddle and by-passed the hotel saving his life.

The Cory-Spencer partnership would last four years ending in 1856. Dr. Spencer practiced in San Jose for thirty years before moving to Florida. He died in 1882 at the age of seventy six.

Pioneer Physicians of Los Gatos

By Gerald E. Trobough, MD

There were three notable pioneer physicians who assisted Los Gatos in becoming a thriving township in the mid -1800's. Los Gatos had its beginnings when a flour mill was built on the Los Gatos Creek in 1851 by James Alexander Forbes. Forbes, a Welshman, was Vice-counsel of the British Government and was living in Santa Clara during the gold rush. At the time, there was a great demand for flour to make bread for the miners in the gold fields. The Forbes Mill was the first building and business established in Los Gatos. Even though the mill was not very successful, it brought attention to the beautiful area at the base of the Santa Cruz Mountains and attracted many settlers.

Dr. William S. McMurtry

The first physician to settle in the Los Gatos Area was Dr. William S. McMurtry. Born in Kentucky in 1818, Dr. McMurtry took his medical training in Ohio, Kentucky and Indiana. As a young Medic, he enlisted in the army to fight in the Mexican War. When he found out his regiment was to participate as Infantry, he left the army and joined the Texas Rangers and fought in the Battle of Monterey.

Dr. McMurtry was to begin a medical practice in Baton Rouge, Louisiana in 1848. That year gold was discovered in California and like many others he "caught the gold bug". With a party of 30 men, he traveled through Mexico and arrived in San Francisco on May 24,1849. He immediately went to work at the gold mines but had only mediocre success. After a short stint in the quartz mines in Grass Valley, Dr. McMurtry migrated to the Southern Santa Clara County town called Lexington (now covered by the Lexington Reservoir) and established a successful lumber business.

In 1868, McMurtry moved to Los Gatos and with a partner (J. W. McMillan) bought a half interest in the Forbes Mill. They remodeled the mill and made it 20 feet taller allowing the mill to produce 100 barrels of flour a day. The price of flour which was $50 a barrel when the mill opened, dropped to $5 a barrel and the business was not profitable. McMurtry was an important businessman in the early years of Los Gatos and along with Dr. Knowles and Dr. Gober he signed the documents to incorporate Los Gatos. The Town of Los Gatos was incorporated on August 10, 1887. Prior names of Los Gatos were Redwood Township, Forbestown and Forbes Mill. In 1895, McMurtry opened an office to practice medicine on East Main Street. Dr. McMurtry died on December 8, 1904 at the age of 86.

Dr. Frank Knowles

Dr Frank Knowles was the first full time physician to practice in Los Gatos. He arrived in 1883. Dr. Knowles was born on 3/2/1858 in Illinois and trained at Rush Medical College in Chicago. After graduation, he established a medical practice in Los Gatos. At that time, there were few people in Los Gatos. Many of his patients lived in the Santa Cruz mountains that he accessed with horse and buggy, When the brush was too thick, he would un-hitch the buggy and travel on horseback or on foot to reach his patients. His devotion to his patients , his profession, and his work in the community made him extremely popular. His office was located over Green's Pharmacy.

Knowles also loved farming. He established a 42 acre orchard in the current Vasona Lake area raising apricots, prunes, peaches and grapes. He was an original share.holder, director and vice-president of the First National Bank of Los Gatos. Dr. Knowles died in November, 1936.

Dr. Frank Gober

Dr. Frank Gober came to Los Gatos in 1884. He was born in Sacramento on November 24, 1858. His medical training included one year at Cooper Medical School in San Francisco. He left the west coast and completed his schooling in New York graduating from Belview Medical College in 1884. He married Annette Bean, daughter of John Bean who invented a spray pump. Bean's manufacturing company later became known as FMC, a major industry in the Santa Clara Valley The Gober's built a beautiful home on the corner of Bean and Santa Cruz Avenues in Los Gatos. After 35 years of marriage, Annette died in 1921 leaving 2 children. The stately mansion was razed in1938 in order to build a supermarket.

Gober established several medical offices in downtown Los Gatos, but a large

part of his practice was in the Saratoga mountains. He, like Dr. Knowles, traveled by horseback or horse and buggy to diagnose and treat patients. His medical "territory" ranged from Los Gatos and Saratoga to Boulder Creek in Santa Cruz County. Often he was in the mountains for days at a time doing surgery and providing post operative care or waiting to deliver a baby. For Dr. Gober to find his way, the residents would hang lanterns on the roads or trails. When he reached the last lantern, he would yell out and someone would come to him and lead him to the ill patient. He was lovingly referred to as "Los Gatos' Horse and Buggy Doctor"

Dr. Gober practiced medicine in Los Gatos tor 58 years and retired in 1935. He died in 1942, at the age of 84.

KEELEY INSTITUTE

By Gerald E. Trobough, MD

One of the first hospitals established in Los Gatos was the Keeley Institute. It was built on East Main Street in 1891 by building contractor, Herman Sund. The hospital was owned by Dr. Leslie Keeley who was a graduate of Rush Medical College and a retired Civil War physician. Dr. Keeley became interested in treating alcoholism during that war and established over 200 clinics across the nation and Europe.

Dr. Keeley's first clinic was established in Dwight, Illinois in 1880. The mission of the clinics was to treat alcohol, tobacco, and opiate addiction. He pioneered medical studies and a treatment for alcoholism. His treatment for addiction was called the "gold cure" because he used oral bichloride of gold. However, a chemical analysis of the oral tonic revealed 27.55°/o alcohol, ammonium chloride, aloin, and tincture of cinchoa but no gold. The injections contained strychnine, atropine and boracic acid and no gold. The magic cure, however, was probably Group Therapy which he introduced to medicine. He told patients that gold chloride and alcohol didn't mix and the combination of the two could be harmful to their health. His clinics were recognized as some of the most advanced rehabilitation centers in the country. Keeley published numerous articles and pamphlets about his clinics and reported his successes. He also wrote several books on alcohol and drug addiction. "The Morphine Eater" was published in 1881 and the " Non-Heredity of Inebriates" in 1896.

The Los Gatos facility remained open for four years and closed in 1895. During that brief period of time over 1000 patients were treated, many who came from long distances. Documents suggest that fifty of these patients were from the Los Gatos area. The treatments lasted 6 weeks and the cost was $25 to $50 a week. The treatments were the same in all the clinics. The whiskey ration was quickly reduced. Eight ounces was allowed on the first day, six ounces on the second day, four ounces on the third day, and none after that. Injections were given four times a day and the oral "gold tonic" was given every two hours.

After the facility closed, Sund donated the use of the building to the town of Los Gatos for its new Town Hall. Other Keeley Institutes in California were built in Auburn and Riverside. Dr Keeley died in the Los Angeles area in 1900 at the age of 63. At the time of his death, his estate was estimated to be greater than one million dollars.

Here Come The Lady Physicians

By Michael Shea MD

The first woman to graduate from medical school in the United States was Elizabeth Blackwell. She graduated from Geneva Medical College in Upstate New York in 1849. Shortly thereafter, The Women's Medical College of Pennsylvania in Philadelphia opened in 1850. This model for women's medical schools was copied in Boston, New York, Detroit, and Chicago. Later, medical schools of all three systems (allopaths, homeopaths, and eclectics) became coed.

In California, the University of California Medical School opened its doors to women applicants in 1873. The Medical School of the Pacific did likewise in 1877. Official recognition of women as medical practitioners did not take place until 1876, when Governor Irwin signed the Medical Practice Law.

There were, however, female physicians who arrived in California well before this date.

The first was Dr. Eliza Pfeifer Stone. German born and educated, she arrived in Nevada City in 1857 and relocated to San Francisco in 1863. The second was Dr. Rebecca A. Howard, arriving in San Francisco in 1864, directly after receiving her degree at Philadelphia. Her husband was killed at the battle of Bull Run and her daughter, Dr. Kate I. Howard was to become a University of California medical graduate in 1885. Dr Euthanasia S. Meade(1836-1895) (yes, that is her actual first name) was the third.

Dr. Meade's attention was first drawn to the profession during the last years of the Civil War. At St. Joseph's Hospital in Philadelphia, she gained her first exposure to medicine by taking care of wounded soldiers. Four years after the war, she graduated from The Women's College of Pennsylvania. She practiced under her preceptor, Dr. Wilson in Philadelphia, visiting the hospitals and gaining practical experience.

In 1869, she arrived in San Francisco. but found San Jose a more favorable climate for her asthma and thus became San Jose's first female certified physician.

She, along with five other women physicians, were admitted to the State Medical Society, which convened in San Francisco in 1786. The vote was even,but it took the president of the society, Dr. A. B. Nixon, to cast the deciding affirmative vote.

Dr. Meade was instrumental in forming the Women's Medical Club of the Pacific, a statewide medical society. She was elected the first president and delivered the inaugural address at the opening convention.

Her junior partner for three years was Dr. Elizabeth Gallimore (see picture). She was born locally and received her diploma from Cooper Medical College in San Francisco in 1887. For fifteen months, she was a resident physician at the Children's Hospital in San Francisco. She also attended a post graduate course at the New England Hospital in Boston. She returned to San Jose and joined Dr. Meade in her medical practice. Dr. Gallimore served as recording secretary for the County Medical Society for many years. She enjoyed the respect and admiration of all her colleagues in San Jose.

Enrollment in the United States medical schools for 2013 was 83,472. 44,525(53%) were men and 38,948(47%) were women. The ladies have come a long way from 1849.

The Cholera Epidemic in San Jose, California, 1850

By Elizabeth Ahrens-Kley

As cholera swept across Europe and the eastern U.S. in the mid-1800s, thousands perished from the so-called "noxious vapors," a dangerous miasma, or "bad air" thought to be the deadly and unavoidable source of the illness. Death struck with terrifying suddenness, killing a random few to hundreds at one time. Those infected could perish within a few hours. Every sort of cure was proposed, but none worked with any notable success. Thousands are thought to have died while crossing the plains to California. The doctors in San Jose who actively fought the disease in 1850, Dr. Benjamin Cory, Dr. John Townsend, and Dr. Louis Bascom, were no more successful in their fight against it than the most famed doctors in London.

Dr. Cory

It was not known that bacteri-

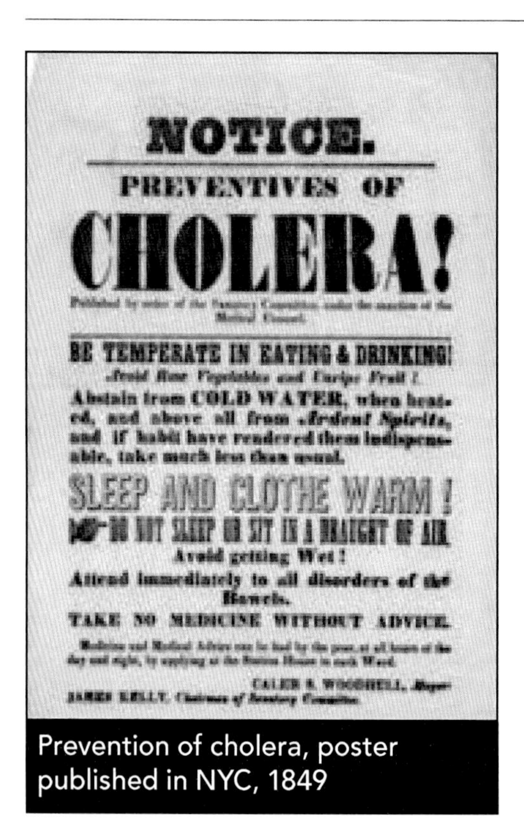

Prevention of cholera, poster published in NYC, 1849

ally-contaminated water, from ponds, wells, rivers, or, as most certainly was the case in San Jose, a large ditch known as the Acequia Madre, was the likely culprit. In earlier times, a dam had been built above the pueblo to collect water in a pond supplied by the Canoas Creek. The pond fed water into the Acequia, which meandered through the town, providing irrigation for agriculture, as well as being the source of domestic water. The tributaries functioned as collectors for runoff and collection of sewage.

As thousands of gold seekers streamed into town in 1849, as well as politicians and legislators (San Jose being designated the new capital of California), a violent outbreak of the disease was preordained. No sanitation infrastructure existed and the serious lack of hygienic conditions allowed the disease to spread with vicious rapidity in November and December of 1850. Residents fled the town en masse and as suddenly as it began, by mid December, the brutal crisis had ended.

Of the three doctors who worked day and night tending to those in need, only Dr. Cory continued practicing medicine in the long-term. Dr. John Townsend and wife Elizabeth, famed as members of the Murphy party, which crossed the plains in 1844, both contracted the disease while treating patients and succumbed. Dr. Louis Bascom and Dr. Cory continued their partnership (having worked together during the epidemic) for a short time, but only two years later, Dr. Bascom bought 135 acres of farm land, thereafter registering himself as "farmer" instead of "physician." Dr. Bascom is mainly remembered nowadays for having sold a strip of his land to the town, which is presently known as Bascom Avenue. He lived until 1881, and Dr. Cory continued his practice for another 46 years, until his death in 1896.

A Famous Grizzly Bear Attack in 1854

By Michael A. Shea, MD

Charles Henry McKiernan built his ranch in the mountains southwest of Los Gatos, in June of 1851. Mountain Charley, his local name, was more of a hunter than a rancher. He hunted deer and sold the venison to buyers in San Francisco. He also was known for his grizzly bear hunting.

Grizzly bears abounded in the area. According to one Franciscan padre in Santa Cruz, they were numerous, "prowling about in herds, like hogs on a farm." These animals, known for their ferocity, could reach eight feet in height and weigh up to 800 pounds.

On May 11, 1854, Charley and a man named Taylor were deer hunting near his ranch, when they encountered a very large grizzly bear. Taylor fired the first shot and missed. Charley fired and the ball struck the bear in the head, but did not penetrate. The bear, stunned, fell to the ground. Charley struck him on the head with his gun, breaking the barrel. The bear immediately arose, with his huge jaw wide open, made a snap at Charley. He crushed his skull and tore out a piece of bone just above the left eye. After biting the victim on both arms, the bear went crashing through the brush, heading down the mountain.

Dr. T. J. Ingersoll was called to attend to Charley, and the following is his actual account of the incident and the treatment:

"My partner, Dr. A. W. Bell, went out and found him the next morning about sunrise, with the front part of his head terribly mangled and some wounds on both arms, but rational. The piece of skull taken out by the animal was sent in with a request that I should have a plate of silver made and come out immediately to assist in dressing the wound. Making all necessary preparations, I hastened to the patient, getting there about 9:00 p.m., when I found that the piece of bone of os frontis sent in was only about half of the bone taken out. On the next morning, returned to San Jose to have another plate made, sufficiently large to cover the brain

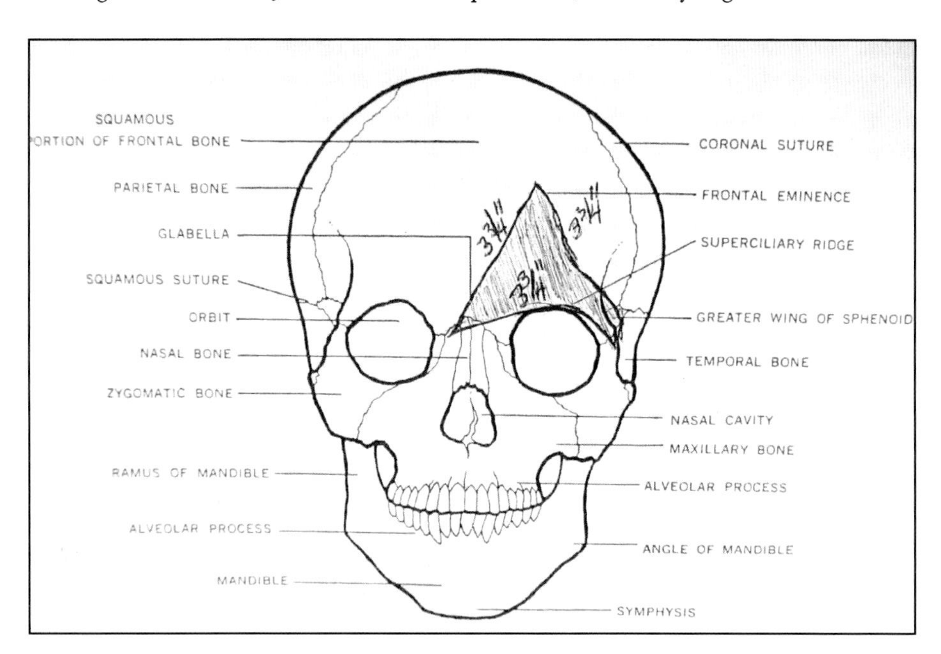

– getting back to the patient the same day at 8:00 p.m. Dr. Bell and myself proceeded to apply the plate and dress the wounds; got through about 11:00 p.m.

The part of the bone detached was all that portion of the os frontis, above the left eye and nose, and in the orbit about three-fourths of an inch – taking a portion of the zygomatic process, ranging up about four inches parallel with the coronal suture, from that point, irregularly to the right of the root of the nose, about three-and-three-quarter inches on each of the three sides. The muscles and integument were brought together and secured with sutures – soon closed by first intention, with the exception of two or three points for the matter to flow, and where the parts would not meet. By general bleeding and cold applications to the head, very little disturbance took place.

After the expiration of a week, I found that the plate was irritating the parts so much that it was impossible for them to become sound, and immediately took it out, very much against the wishes of the patient.

I would mention that it was at the urgent solicitation of the patient that the plate was used in the first place, notwithstanding the expostulations of his physicians. The wound healed kindly, with the exception of the two points on each side of the nose, where there were some spicula of bone, which kept up some irritation and discharging of matter.

The left eyeball, in consequence of the muscles above it contracting, not having sufficient support, turned up about eight degrees. General health was good.

Some twelve months after the events related above, the patient, having suffered from an intolerable pain in the head, came into town and consulted Dr. Spencer and myself. It was decided to perform an operation.

Accordingly, we with some others, waited for him at the National Hotel, where after administering chloroform, the operation took place. We cut down and found a deep-seated abscess under the anterior lobe of the brain, at least two-inches deep, above and behind the nasal process, which was discharging through the small sinus above the left eye. The operation had the desired effect – the abscess soon got well, and the patient was relieved of the pain he had been suffering some time before.

His health is good, but as a matter of course, his face is much disfigured. He does not think that his mind or memory has been affected by the injury he received from the bear, but sometimes complains of a dull sensation in the region of the brain."

Mountain Charley survived another 38 years, passing away January 16, 1892.

ORIFICIAL SURGERY

By Michael A. Shea, MD

The most influential of the nineteenth century American unorthodox medical sects was the homeopathic movement. It was founded by a German physician, Samuel Hahnemann (1755-1843), and became very popular among the middle and upper class of the United States.

An advertisement for the 1913 meeting of the American Association of Orificial Surgeons (author's collection).

One of the most interesting and bizarre practices to emerge from homeopathy was orificial surgery. The origin of this practice came from Edwin Hartley Pratt (1849-1930), an Illinois homeopathic general practitioner and surgeon. He believed that chronic diseases (physical and mental) could be cured by surgical procedures involving bodily orifices. These openings were: nares, mouth, anus and rectum, introitus, urethra, vagina, and cervix. He believed that the basis for this theory was that the sympathetic nervous system, which terminated at all the above orifices, was responsible for the well being of all bodily functions. Any disturbance at these various portals (such as inflammation, cysts, sphincter rigidity, etc.) would cause disease in more distal parts of the body.

In 1886, Pratt published the first article on his philosophy, and one year later, a lengthy monograph followed. This new concept attracted a significant number of American physicians and led to the national organization of the American Association of Orificial Surgeons. In mid 1892, *The Journal of Orificial Surgery* began publication with Pratt as editor-in-chief.

Locally, Dr. R. E. Freeman, of Los Gatos, was known as one of the best orificial surgeons in our area. He graduated from The Hahnemann College of Philadelphia in 1886.

The surgical procedures practiced by Dr. Pratt and his followers included anal sphincter dilatation, rectal papillae scraping or excision, hemorrhoidectomy, male and female circumcision, hymenectomy, excision of the cervix, D&C, and vaginal hysterectomy. These operations were often done in combination, as Dr. Pratt's theory espoused the idea that multiple sites of orificial irritation were the basis for the disease afflicting the patient.

The conditions ostensibly cured by the above operations were tuberculosis, asthma, constipation, eczema, dysmenorrhea, uterine atrophy, fundal malposition, dyspareunia, insanity, depression, epilepsy, paralysis, and others.

The appeal of orificial surgery was popular for two or three decades and paralleled the success of homeopathic therapeutics.

The decline of these practices began in 1901, when the *Journal of Orificial Surgery* abruptly stopped publication with little explanation. Annual meetings of the American Association of Orificial Surgery continued through the early 1900s, but by the 1920s, they had ceased and the practice of this unusual branch of medicine was over.

Origins of the Medical Societies

By Gerald E. Trobough, MD

In the early part of the 191h century, medical education was in a deplorable state. There were approximately 450 proprietary medical schools. Their primary aim was to collect tuition from students for the privilege of attending lecture for 10 -20 weeks. There were no entrance requirements beyond the ability to pay for the courses. There were few examinations and the resulting diploma was accepted as a license to practice medicine.

American Medical Association (AMA)

The American Medical Association was organized on May 7, 1847. This "drastic measure" was to establish standards of care and improve medical education. A program of medical ethics was introduced as well as the promotion of public service.

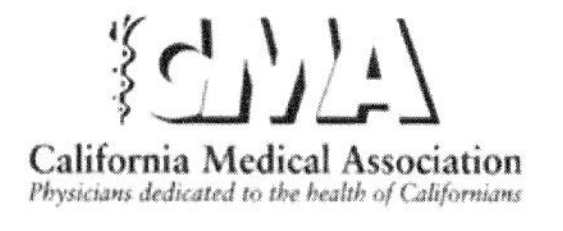

The first meeting was at the Academy of Natural Sciences in Philadelphia, Pennsylvania. The 250 delegates present elected Dr. Nathaniel Chapman as its first president. An initial committee of nine doctors, headed by Dr. Nathan Smith Davis was established to develop recommendations to improve medical education. Dr. Davis was the first African American graduate from Rush Medical School. He is often credited as the father of the AMA and was the first editor of JAMA.

Despite the good intentions of the AMA, the society had no vested authority to change policy of the proprietary medical schools. However, the AMA set standards and pointed the way towards reform.

California Medical Society (CMA)

The Medical Society of the State of California was established in 1856 behind the leadership of Dr. Elias Cooper and Dr. Thomas Logan. They wrote letters to their colleagues asking for support of a state organization that promoted medical education "and develop, in the highest degree, the scientific truths embodied in the profession". Another goal of the society was to root out quackery.

Their first meeting was March 12, 1856 at Pioneer Hall located on J Street in Sacramento. The first president was Dr. Benjamin Franklin Keene from El Dorado County. Unfortunately, Dr. Keene died a few months after taking office. The second president was Dr. Elias Cooper from San Francisco. Dr. Cooper was the head of the Medical Department of the University of the Pacific which was California's first medical school.

Dr. Thomas Logan, a Sacrament physician, assisted in the formation of the medical society of California. He became the first president of the AMA from the west coast. He brought the national AMA meeting to San Francisco in 1871. Logan also promoted state public health departments and he lobbied for county medical societies. His role in the California Public Health Department is legendary. Dr. Logan felt it imperative that physicians track births, diseases, deaths and their causes. In 1870, he authored a law to establish the State Board of Health. It was the second state to have a Public Health Board. Logan also promoted childhood vaccinations.

Another important person in the early CMA history was Dr. John Frederick Morris. Dr. Morris set up the first credentials committee of the CMA in an attempt to prevent unqualified physicians from practicing in the state. He is also credited with starting the first journal of the medical society in 1873. It was called The California State Journal of Medicine.

The Medical Society of California was re-named California Medical Association in 1923.

Santa Clara County Medical Society

The County Medical Society was organized on May 9, 1870 by nine physicians with a stated goal of"alleviation of human suffering by stimulating its members to acquire and perfect medical knowledge." It was a loosely organized association. The society was re-organized along formal lines by twelve physicians on August 12, 1876. The new stated objectives were "discuss developments in medicine and also fight itinerant quacks and charlatans flourishing on credulous human nature."

The meetings were held on the second Tuesday of each month. For at least ten years, the meetings were held in the offices of Drs. Cory and Kelly. Thereafter the meetings were rotated in the offices of other participating physicians. Papers were often read and discussed. Case histories were presented and commented upon by the members. The Society worked hard to identify "pretenders of medical knowledge" and drive them out of the valley.

The County Medical Society was also instrumental in establishing a City Board of Health in 1899. It exposed unsanitary conditions that affected public health. Dr. J.R. Curnow was elected health officer. He established an excellent city sewer system that practically eliminated typhoid fever and diphtheria in the county.

These Medical Societies have helped shape medical care in the 19th and 20th centuries and will continue to do so in this 21st century.

America's Greatest Surgeon?

By Gerald E. Trobough, MD

Many American surgeons have contributed knowledge and new techniques to improve medical and surgical care in the past 150 years. Many believe that the greatest contributor was Dr. William Stewart Halsted.

As one of the "Big Four" founding professors at Johns Hopkins Medical School, Halsted was credited with significant surgical achievements during his lifetime. Following medical school at Columbia University in 1877, Halsted studied in Europe under Dr. Billroth, Europe's pre-eminent surgeon. He learned antiseptic and hemostatic techniques and later brought them to the United States.

Dr. Halsted went into private practice in New York City in 1880. In 1881, Halsted made medical history by performing the first blood transfusion. He was called to see his sister after she had given birth. She had a massive postpartum hemorrhage and was moribund from blood loss. He withdrew his own blood with a syringe and injected it into his sister's vein. (ABO blood types were not identified until1900.) The amount ofblood transferred was not recorded but she survived.

The following year, Halsted was notified that his mother was critically ill. Her condition mystified her physicians. He examined his mother and determined she had cholecystitis. He operated on her immediately atop the kitchen table. Halsted opened the gall bladder and removed six stones and drained the purulent material. His mother recovered uneventfully. This marked one of the earliest successful gall bladder surgeries.

Other great accomplishments by Halsted include:

1. Use of cocaine for local anesthesia.
2. The development of"Halsted Surgical Principles" that are still espoused today as well as aseptic technique, gentle handling of tissue, scrupulous hemostasis, tension free closures, and anatomically proper alignment.
3. Pioneered the use of surgeon caps, scrub suits and latex surgical gloves. Before Halsted, street clothes were worn and un-gloved hands were common practice while performing surgery.
4. Developed the first radical mastectomy for breast cancer in 1889. His en-bloc technique resulted in decreased local recurrences and many patients were cured or had longer disease free intervals than prior surgical techniques.
5. Develop a new technique for hernia repair. Prior to 1889, there was a 100% recurrence rate. The rate after Halsted's procedure was 8%.
6. Developed techniques for safe thyroid surgery and arterial aneurysm surgery
7. Developed the first surgical residency program in the United States.
8. Created a humane and scientific experimental laboratory that trained medical students and residents in new techniques that advanced the science of surgery.
9. Halsted's residents included such notables as Harvey Cushing, "the father of Neurosurgery"; Walter Dandy who developed pneumo-ventriculography and was known as "most important neurosurgeon in the world"; Hugh Young, known as "the father of urology"; and Joseph Bloodgood, "the father of surgical pathology."

William Halsted was often called the "father of modern surgery." What is most amazing, Halsted realized all of these accomplishments as a drug addict. He became addicted to cocaine in 1885 while studying its use as a local anesthetic. In 1886, in an a attempt to cure cocaine addiction, morphine was used as a substitute. This treatment failed and Halsted subsequently became addicted to both cocaine and morphine. Despite taking massive doses of morphine (195 mg/d), only two or three of his closest friends ever knew of his addictions.

First Hospital in San Jose

By Gerald E. Trobough, MD

In 1854, the Santa Clara County Board of Supervisors and the Town Council of San Jose met and decided the area needed a hospital. Rampant diseases such as tuberculosis , diphtheria, cholera, and small pox infections were killing many citizens and there were no hospitals in the area.

In 1855, the County rented a house on Second Street called the "Old Levy Property" for $40 a month. They hired a physician to care for patients for $50 a month. It was soon realized the house was too small to accommodate the influx of patients.

County Hospital 1875

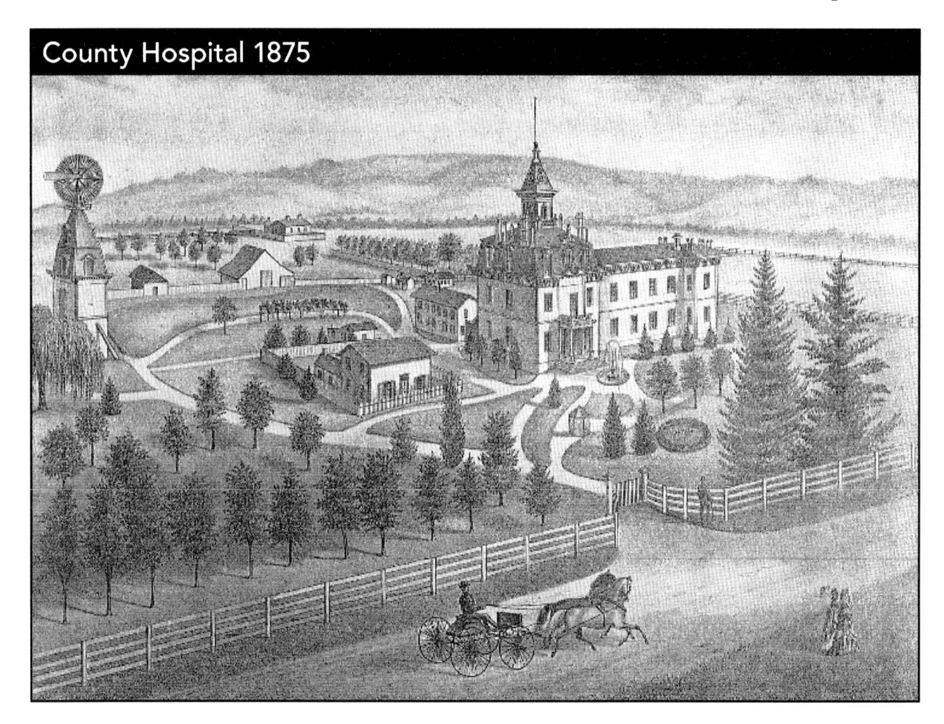

The County then purchased “The Sutter House”, a larger home located Northeast of San Jose. The house and the 25 acre parcel was purchased for $5500. However, after three months , the owners failed to produce a valid deed and the purchase was rescinded in February 1856.

The County then made the decision to ‘farm out” patients to various homes and buildings in the area. They hired Dr. G. B. Crane to provide medical and surgical care, and medications to the indigent sick. His stipend was $4,600 a year to attend no more than seven patients a day.

In 1860, the necessity of a hospital building became increasingly apparent. Santa Clara County purchased 12 acres of land from a farmer Hiram Cahill for $4,000. This land was located on Dupont and South Streets (now Park and Montgomery Streets). They enlarged and refurbished the original building for the main Hospital. They constructed another facility to house patients with infectious diseases south of the main building near the Los Gatos Creek referred to as “The Pest House”. The Hospital occupied these buildings until it was deemed too small. It took the community leaders three years to find another location. Under the leadership of Drs. Ben Cory and A.J. Cory, the Board made the decision to purchase land for a new hospital.

In 1871, the County paid John Conner $12,400 for 114 acres in West San Jose, called West Willows. It was located on San Jose -Los Gatos Road. (later called Infirmary Road and known today as Bascom Ave). The buildings on the Cahill site were moved to the new hospital site. These were used until the new hospital was built. The Cahill property was divided into lots that sold for $4,518.

A three story hospital building was completed in 1875 at a cost of $14,533.70 and was named “Santa Clara County Infirmary”. The builder was W.O Breytogel and the architects of the Gothic style building were Mr. Lenzen and Gash. It was the first hospital in the San Francisco Bay Area. It had six wards that accommodated 65 patients. They built 3 other buildings that housed another 50 patients in nine wards. Other structures were built including a water tower, pest house and a potters field (a common grave for the burial of unknown or indigent persons). The hospital opened in 1876. In 1884, 81 acres of the hospital tract were sold to different parties. The remaining 33 acres was used for the hospital. The money accrued from these sales amounted to $14,728 that was used to cover the cost of the hospital construction.

The first director of the hospital was Dr. George Crane from 1855 to 1865. The second hospital director from 1865 to 1876 was Dr. Andrew Jackson Cory, the younger brother of Ben Cory. He oversaw the construction of the new hospital. His salary was $1,500 a year. Dr. A. McMahon was director in 1876-1878, Dr. J. B. Cox in 1878-1880 and Benjamin Cory in 1880-1882.

The hospital has remained in its current location since 1876. It has been rebuilt, remodeled and enlarged many times over the past 138 years to become one of the premier hospitals in Northern California. The Hospital was extensively damaged in the 1906 earthquake. The rebuilding was completed in 1907 and the facility was renamed Santa Clara County Hospital. It became a teaching hospital for nursing students in 1905 and for physicians in 1908. The first medical and surgical intern was Dr. Doxy Wilson a graduate of Cooper Medical School (later Stanford Medical School). Dr. Wilson later became administrator and was Director of Medical Institutions of Santa Clara County from 1913 -1940.

In the 1910's, the first tuberculosis sanitarium was built. It was expanded in 1918 and 1927. Pediatrics and Maternity units were built in 1939 and 1940. Other buildings housed an Emergency Department, Laboratory, Men's and Women's Medicine, Surgery and Orthopedics. The next major building expansion occurred north of the "Old County Hospital" main building in the early 1960's. It was a 7 story tower and was called the "New County Hospital". It also included a large clinic building that housed a new Laboratory, Emergency Department, and office space for Interns and Residents to see outpatients known as "the Clinics". During the 1960's many departments of the County Hospital developed affiliations with Stanford Medical School. In the 1970's it was renamed Santa Clara Valley Medical Center.

In 1970, construction began on a four story Rehabilitation Center that replaced the "Old County Hospital" Main Entrance. This facility allowed the Hospital to care for and develop expertise in treating spinal cord injuries. New construction in 1990 resulted in the West Wing that housed a new adult ICU and neonatal ICU. In 1999, a new main Hospital was constructed.

Santa Clara Valley Medical Center has had a "number of firsts" in its long history. It was the first organized hospital in the San Francisco Bay Area (1876). It was one of the first hospitals to be accreditated by the Joint Commission (1952). It operates the only federally designated spinal cord injury center in Northern California. The hospital is a level one adult trauma center (only 3 other centers in Northern California), a level one Pediatric trauma center (only 2 other centers in Northern California) and a burn center (only 3 other centers in · Northern California). Other "Centers of Excellence" at this outstanding facility are a level one Neonatal ICU and it is licensed as a primary Stroke Center by the Joint Commission.

The History Of O'Connor Hospital

By Michael A. Shea MD

Judge Myles O'Connor

Myles O'Connor was born May 8, 1823 in Abbey Leix, Ireland. From this tiny hamlet, fifty miles from Dublin, his family migrated to London when he was two years old.

In 1838,at the age of fourteen, they moved to America. They lived in St. Louis where Uncle Jeremiah O'Connor was well established. (he had given the city a large grant of land and donated property for the original site of St. Louis University.)

Myles, a quiet studious boy, began work in a local lawyer's office when he was nineteen. At age twenty three, he graduated with honors from St. Louis University Law School and immediately began practice.

In April of 1849, the young attorney, lured by gold tales and the thought of practicing his craft in a new frontier, left St. Louis, bound for California. He was part of a wagon train, where his assignment was chef. One hundred twenty two days and two thousand miles later, he arrived at Sutter's Fort. He settled down in Grass Valley where he practiced law and gold mining.

Romance entered Myles life in 1862, when he married a petite widow, Amanda Butler Young. This marriage was to last forty seven years. Fortune smiled on the couple in 1863. O'Connor and two partners discovered the Idaho mine which was to produce a lifetime of wealth for the judge and his wife.

Politics became his third occupation. He was elected to the California State Assembly in 1859 for one term. Later he served as justice of the peace in Grass Valley. He won reelection nine consecutive times. Following this, he won a seat in the state senate which he held for six years.

The next five years found the O'Connors traveling throughout Europe. When they returned to the states, they settled in San Jose.

A long simmering idea to build a home for the aged and the needy, began to take shape in 1887. It would be known as the O'Connor Sanitarium. The construction was left to a long time confidante, Edward McLaughlin. This sanitarium would be used for the care of the sick, a home for the aged, and a school for children. The Daughters of Charity of Saint Vincent de Paul were given control of the sanitarium. Theodore Lenzen, famous for his designs of city hall and many other civic buildings was chosen as the architect. The O'Connor Sanitarium opened its doors in 1889. It was located on a country site, chosen by Judge O'Connor, south of Steven Creek Road, between Meridian and Race Streets. It encompassed 8.395 acres. Sister Severina Brandel of the Daughters of Charity was appointed the first superior.

The building consisted of two stories, made of brick, with sandstone facings. Giant white columns supported the portico over the main entrance. North and south wings stretched toward Meridian Road. The south wing lower floor was a woman's ward and the upper story, the sister's residence. The north wing housed the men's ward, storeroom and kitchen, with the second floor divided into apartments for families. In all, there were forty four rooms and five wards. The basement contained the engine room, furnace, and laundry.

At first, the hospital served more as a home for the aged and infirm. By the end of the century, medicine was advancing in great strides. Doctors were treating patients at the Sanatarium in growing numbers. Sister Raphael Jones, the second superior, began major changes that would convert the Sanatarium into a hospital. Carpets were replaced by sanitary flooring, high hospital beds went in, and electricity replaced the old acetylene lighting system.

By 1902, an operating room was set up, north of the main entrance. Instruments were sterilized in boiling water on the kitchen range in the basement. In 1906, operations had increased to such a point, that a completely new surgical wing was constructed, north of the main unit. It was here that thousands of operations were performed for almost half a century.

By 1910, an isolation building was added for contagious diseases. Departments now included x-ray, medical, obstetrical, electrotherapeutic, surgical, clinical labora-

tory, and pharmacy. The last renovation was the conversion of the O'Connor House into a pediatric ward,(It had been added to the Hospital in the late eighteen hundreds.

Feeling the need for more space, a building drive was started in 1947. The location of the new hospital was a twenty four acre pear orchard, located off Forest Avenue. On January 23, 1954, the new six million dollar O'Connor Hospital admitted the first patients.

ADDENDUM

Myles Poore O'Connor died on June 9, 1909, due to a series of strokes. He was eighty six. Amanda O'Connor past away April 11. 1926 at the age of ninety. They had no children.

The History Of San Jose Hospital

By Michael A. Shea MD

On May 25, 1921, forty three physicians signed a statement of intent to found a new hospital in San Jose. This was done in response to the merger of Columbia and East Columbia Hospitals, effectively reducing the number of hospital beds in San Jose.

The cost was $450,000, raised by community subscription. The location was known as the Joseph Lee home site, on the north side of east Santa Clara Street between fourteenth and fifthteenth streets. The main item of landscaping was a giant redwood tree that Lee brought down from the Santa Cruz mountains and planted in front of his house in 1860.

The grand opening was June fourth, 1923. This was the third major hospital in

San Jose (the first was Santa Clara County Hospital and the second O'Connor Hospital). The three story structure sat on a spacious lawn with a basement and a penthouse, which housed the surgical suite. The construction material was reinforced concrete in order to resist earthquakes and fire. There were forty four private rooms and nine four bed wards, plus a nursery.

The private rooms were plush with carpet and drapes, color schemes, telephone, and a silent signal system connected to the nurses station. There also was a lavatory in each room. The penthouse surgical suite had five operating rooms and two solariums, landscaped with gardens. The basement housed the x-ray and fluoroscopy unit, lab, emergency room, pharmacy, morgue, linens, bake shop, kitchen and two cafeterias(one for the doctors and one for the nurses). It was described as the first truly modern hospital in the country.

The hospital had a board of directors, a medical staff, and an administration. The first president of the medical staff was Thomas L. Blanchard. Doctors paid a membership fee of one hundred dollars and annual dues were six dollars. There was no departmentalization at that time.

Two thirds of admissions were for surgery- mainly T&A's, hysterectomies and appendectomies. One third of admissions were for medical indications such as nonsurgical orthopedic problems and childbirth.

Quality assurance was accomplished by monthly staff meetings. Surgical mortality was very good. Obstetrical maternal mortality was not so good. The rate was 1.5% and newborn mortality was 4%. These both changed for the better after Dr. Alson Shufelt (the first obstetrician in San Jose) began his practice at this time. In 1925, forty percent of deliveries were done in the hospital. By 1929, that figure had changed to seventy-five percent and most of these were done at San Jose Hospital.

The first administrator was Henry J. Bostwick. He was succeeded by Wm. P. Butler in 1932. Mr. Butler guided the hospital through the depression years and succeeded in making it a nonprofit institution. This encouraged endowments and donations.

During World War 11, the population of service people increased in San Jose. This increased the need for hospital beds. Mr. Butler responded by decreasing hospital stays, turning private rooms into semiprivate rooms, and and creating more four bed wards. He also started a new industrial accident ward called the Derby Ward.

Post war, hospital census increased again, with deliveries at ten per day, and this with only two delivery rooms.

In 1946, four barracks were purchased and moved across the street yielding an additional thirty-four beds. Using Hill-Burton funds(Federal Government loans), the hospital added beds by extending the east wing northward and adding a story in front of the west wing. Capacity now was 240 beds.

David Olsson became the next administrator when Butler died from a heart attack in 1951. He set his sights on increasing the number of beds by not only adding a four story 120 bed addition to the west wing but also purchased Alum Rock Hospital(67 beds). However, most doctors did not use the new acquisition, and it became an extended care facility.

In 1968, a 2.7 million dollar, 252 bed building was constructed as a separate unit at San Jose Hospital and used for extended care and inpatient psychiatry.

1970 marked the merger of Doctors Hospital on the Alameda with San Jose Hospital. The medical staff was not happy. They were not told of the merger and did not approve of the quality of care that Doctors Hospital was known for. Renamed Park Alameda Hospital, it continuously bled money from San Jose Hospital and was finally sold to the city and was used as an alcohol rehab unit.

1974 saw the arrival of John Aird. He came with a masters degree in health administration. He was in his thirties and was one of the youngest hospital administrators in the country. Some of his positive measures were (1) the closure of Park-Alameda Hospital (2) closure of the nursing school (3) The CAPI Unit(adolescent psychiatric inpatient center) (4) remodeling of the Emergency Room). Also in 1974, Stanley Skillicorn MD became the director of medical education. His quality of care program won national acclaim.

The 1970's also saw increased government regulations and decreased reimbursement to hospitals (e.g. PSRO'S, HSA- Health System Agencies).

In 1976, Robert Brueckner was appointed day to day administrator and John Aird took charge of planning and development. The name of the hospital also changed to San Jose Health Center, reflecting a broader role in dealing with the health care system.

The first surgicare center in the Valley opened in 1976. It was founded by Dr. James Dickson, an anesthesiologist, and later sold to San Jose Hospital.

A Family Practice Residency Program was founded at the hospital by Dr. Lee Blanchard and was very successful.

An Alternative Birth Center was started at San Jose Hospital in the same time frame. This allowed mothers to labor and deliver in the same room. It had a home like atmosphere. It proved to be very popular with patients and soon spread to other hospitals.

Time, however, was starting to run out for San Jose's third hospital. The downtown area was starting to be adversely affected by suburban growth in homes and shopping malls. New hospitals were being built in the outlying areas of San Jose.

All of these factors led to the financial instability of San Jose Hospital. The doors finally closed in 2006. A vacant lot is all that is left of the hospital that for eighty-three years served the heart of the city and its people.

Tuberculosis Hospitals of Santa Clara Valley

By Gerald E. Trobough, MD

During the early 1900's the most common cause of death was Tuberculosis. Many patients with this disease were sent to the South San Francisco Bay Area because of it's "healing climate." The first effective treatment of Tuberculosis occurred in health resorts referred to as Sanitariums. The first Sanitarium in the United States was founded by Dr. Edward Livingston Trudeau in Saranac Lake, New York in 1885. The treatment was called a rest cure. Patients were prescribed increased rest,

good nutrition, sunshine and open air. The facility was called the Adirondack Cottage Sanitarium.

The first Sanitarium in the Santa Clara Valley was located on Montevina Road, 2 miles South of Los Gatos in the Santa Cruz foothills. It was named The Oaks Sanitarium and was built in 1913. It was owned by a group of physicians who hired Dr. William Voorsanger to be the medical director. Voorsanger, a graduate of Cooper Medical School in San Francisco, had international training in Pulmonary Medicine and was considered an expert in treating Tuberculosis. He founded the San Francisco Tuberculosis association in 1908. In 1917, because of financial problems at the facility, Dr Voorsanger bought out his partners and became the sole owner of the "Oaks".

The Oaks had 60 beds and was established to provide care to TB patients of "small means". The patients were charged only for the cost of food and maintenance. Those eligible for admittance had to have monthly incomes of less than $200. Despite the financial difficulties the Oaks remained open until 1939.

The second Sanitarium in the Valley was the Boonshaft Sanitarium. Louis Boonshaft was a resident physician at The Oaks Sanitarium and was trained by Dr William Voorsanger. He opened the new Sanitarium in 1922 in the San Jose Eastern Foothills. It was billed as a hospital for Diseases of the Lungs and Throat.

The facility later changed its name to the Alum Rock Sanitarium. In 1957 it was remodeled and licensed as a Medical Hospital. In 1958, under the medical directorship of Dr. Gerald Scarborough, the Sanitarium merged with San Jose Hospital. The facility had 19 medical beds and 48 pulmonary beds. It was located on 9 acres on Crothers Road.

The other large Tuberculosis facility was located at Santa Clara County Hospital. The South Wing of the Tuberculosis Sanitarium was built in 1910, the middle wing built in 1918 and the third wing completed in 1927. The facility had a 144 bed Tuberculosis Isolation Ward. In the 1950's, as new antibiotics and other treatments were instituted, the number of Isolation beds decreased. In 1959, the " Old Chest Clinic" was torn down and replaced with a new Psychiatric Building. The last directors of the Tuberculosis ward were Dr. Mort Manson and Dr. Robert Rowan.

UCSF Medical School--The Beginning

By Michael A. Shea MD

The first medical school in California was not UCSF. That honor goes to The Medical Department of the University of the Pacific, founded in 1858 by Elias S. Cooper MD. It was located in San Francisco(population 56,800), with the charter coming from the University of the Pacific, a Methodist Episcopalian college founded in 1851 and located at San Jose. The school, successful at first, faltered at the passing of its founder, Elias Cooper, in 1862.

It was at this time that a successful San Francisco surgeon, Hugh Toland, was putting together a new group of teachers in order to open another medical school. At this news, the Pacific Medical faculty "suspended" its function and joined the Toland group.

On November 1864, the Toland Medical school opened its doors at Toland Hall on Stockton Street near Chestnut, opposite the San Francisco City Hospital. This school would later become UCSF.

The dual faculty arrangement was rough from the start. In 1870, the Cooper faculty led by Dr. Levi Cooper Lane(Elias S. Cooper's nephew) separated themselves from the Toland School. They started their own medical school which, ultimately, would become Stanford Medical School.

The Toland Medical School was successful from the onset. The first class consisted of eight students who attended two four month lecture courses. This plus a year of preceptorship led to the degree of Doctor of Medicine. Tuition cost was one hundred and fifty dollars.{This eight month curriculum gradually increased to four years by 1893}

Subjects studied were: anatomy, medicine, obstetrics and diseases of women and

Toland Hall in the 60's

children,pathology, and chemistry. Gross anatomy dissection, using pauper cadavers, was available to the students when the State approved the dissection statute in 1864.

The Medical School was granted entry to the San Francisco City and County Hospital in 1865, which allowed students access to a large volume of clinical experience. This relationship continues to the present day.

In 1869, the University of California opened its academic doors. Dr. Toland immediately began a courtship of the University. He felt that the perpetuity of his Medical School would require university affiliation. Negotiations failed at one point when the UC Regents rejected the name Toland Medical College. This stumbling block was overcome when the regents named a chair after Dr. Toland and, in 1872 the Toland Medical College became the Medical Department of the University of California.

Today, UCSF operates four major campus sites in San Francisco and one in Fresno.

In 2013, US News and World Report ranked UCSF fourth among research and primary care medical schools. UCSF is the only medical school in the United States to be so ranked in both research and primary care. Dr. Hugh would be proud.

Hugh Huger Toland(1806-1880)

Hugh Toland was born April 16, 1806, the son of a South Carolina planter and banker. At sixteen he worked with a town doctor in the local apothecary shop. He graduated first in his medical school class at Transylvania University at Lexington Kentucky. In 1832,he traveled to Paris for postgraduate study at the Salpetriere.

The following year he returned to Columbia, South Carolina, where he began a highly successful surgical practice. In 1852, California beckoned and he traveled to Mokelume Hill in Calaveras County, where he unsuccessfully pursued gold mining.

He relocated in San Francisco and set up his office at Montgomery and Merchant streets, where he became the city's foremost surgeon. A list of his accomplishments include: vesico-vaginal fistula repair, iridectomy for glaucoma, thyroidectomy, and repair of aneurysms. He founded Toland Medical College in 1864, and transferred the school to The University of California in 1872.

He was also known to send packages of medicine(Iodide of Potash for tuberculosis and other respiratory infections and mercury with a dash of lobelia for syphilis) plus his advice via Wells Fargo messengers to the miners in the Sierra foothills. Some criticized his mail order business but his work as a serious surgeon and medical educator represents his important contribution to California medicine. He died suddenly at age seventy-four of a stroke, while still active in his Montgomery Street practice.

The Origin Of Stanford Medical School

By Michael A. Shea

To discover the roots of Stanford Medical School, we must begin with Dr. Elias Samuel Cooper(1820-1862). Dr. Cooper was a controversial yet able surgeon in Peoria, Illinois, when in 1854 he elected to pursue postgraduate studies in Edinburgh, Scotland. It was here that he expressed his desire to open a medical college in San Francisco(discovered in a letter from Dr. Cooper to his traveling companion Hugh Keenan). His reasons for choosing an area of the country that he had not even been to seem to be found in his writings. He mentions climate and the predicted future growth of the area as some of his reasons. "Great empire to build! Brilliant destiny in future!"

So it was that in 1858, The Medical Department of the University of the Pacific was founded in San Francisco by Dr. Cooper with eighteen trustees. Ten of whom were clergymen and three were doctors(J. S. McClean, B. F. Hadden and Henry Gibbons). The population of California, at that time was under 380,000 and San Francisco about 56,000.

Entrance requirements were one years apprenticeship with a respectable physician or graduation from high school. For medical graduation, two courses of eighteen weeks were necessary, only one of which had to be taken in San Francisco. Tuition was set at $150.

Providentially, there was soon the addition to the faculty of a new member who was ultimately, by his own efforts, to ensure the survival of the school. (The precursor to Stanford Medical School) This was Cooper's nephew, Dr. Levi Cooper Lane(1828-1902) who was appointed Professor of Physiology in 1861.

Elias Cooper died in 1862, succumbing at age 41 to an obscure neurological disorder. Without his leadership, the school's momentum slackened. It was about this time that Dr. Hugh Toland, a member of the current Cooper school faculty announced his plans to open a new medical school. The Toland Medical School (the future UCSF) opened in San Francisco in 1864. Outclassed and outflanked, the Medical School of the University of the Pacific suspended operation while Dr. Lane and several key faculty colleagues accepted the invitation of Dr. Toland to join the faculty of his new school. However , they later regretted their decision and in 1870 withdrew from the Toland School.

Under the leadership of Dr. Lane, they reactivated the Medical Department of the University of the Pacific, which had been suspended from 1865 through 1869.

When their rejuvenated School reopened in 1870, it was located on Stockton Street, south of Geary in San Francisco, next to the laboratories of University(city) College, a Presbyterian School founded in 1860. In 1872, the school became known as The Medical College of the Pacific.

After 1870, the faculty increased in size and competed successfully for students against the Medical Department of the University of California(formerly Toland Medical School). In 1876, each school awarded twenty diplomas.

When the school was reorganized in 1870, Levi Cooper Lane was designated Professor of Surgery and surgical anatomy, a dual appointment formerly held by Elias Samuel Cooper. Lane also assumed the leadership role that Cooper had previously filled in the affairs of the school.

Lane's plan was divulged in 1882, when he donated to the school an impressive new building, constructed with his own private funds. It was located at the corner of Sacramento and Webster streets in San Francisco. (see picture)

That building, said to have no superior in the world for medical education at the time, was in continuous use as a medical school for the next seventy seven years(1882-1959). On moving to the new facility, the school was incorporated as an independent institution and the name changed from Medical College of the Pacific to Cooper Medical College in honor of Lane's Uncle Elias.

Two additional structures were added to the medical school in the early 1890's. The first was to enlarge the teaching facilities and the second was a two hundred bed hospital, located at Clay and Webster Streets, adjacent to the medical school. From this, Dr. Lane establish the Lane Hospital Training School for Nurses, later to become The Stanford School of Nursing.

The final detail in Lane's grand design was in 1898 when the Doctor and Mrs.,. Lane announced a provision in their wills for the founding of the Lane Medical Library, which is open to the present day.

Levi Cooper Lane died in 1902. Just before his death he made it possible for the Cooper Board of Directors to exercise their own judgment for the future of Cooper Medical College. This they did by arranging in 1908 for the transfer of Cooper Medical College and all its property in San Francisco as a gift to Stanford University for the purpose of establishing a medical department in the university.

The first class of students entered The Stanford Medical Department in September 1909. The last class of Cooper students graduated in May 1912 and Cooper Medical College ceased to exist.

In 1959, the Stanford Hospital, the School of Medicine and Stanford Clinics moved to the Stanford Campus in Palo alto.

In 1968, Stanford University purchased the city of Palo Alto's entire interest in the hospital's properties and facilities. The hospital was renamed the Stanford University Hospital.

Since its move to the campus, the School has grown steadily in national status and now holds a respected place in the front ranks of medical education, scientific achievement, and clinical medicine.

LEVI COOPER LANE

(1830-1902)

By Michael A. Shea

Scholar, multi linguist, author, philanthropist, surgeon, and visionary are qualities possessed by Levy Cooper Lane. Is it small wonder that a person with these credentials would be responsible for the origin of Stanford Medical School?

The parents of Lane were orthodox Quakers living north of Cincinnati on a farm, where he was born May 9, 1830. He received his first schooling from his mother,Hannah, and his aunt, Ruth Cooper; then in due time medical teachings from his two physician uncles, Elias Samuel Cooper and Esaias Cooper.

His formal education began at Farmers College near Cincinnati in 1847. This was for one year. Following which, he spent another year at Union College in Schenectady, New York. He did not receive a degree from either school. Thus his remarkable education in classical literature,history and impressive command of Latin, Greek, German, Spanish, and French largely came by way of independent and tutorial study.

Tracking his chronological studies, we find him in Hendersonville, Illinois, serving a medical apprenticeship under uncle Esaias. This occurred over a three year period. He received his MD degree from Jefferson Medical College at Philadelphia in 1851.

Dr. Lane then spent three years in the practice of his craft, one with Uncle Elias in Peoria and two years with uncle Esaias in Henderson, Illinois.

Tiring of rural general practice, he moved to the east coast in 1854 to become house surgeon to the Lying-in Department of the New York Emigrant Hospital. This hospital was located on Ward's Island, New York City.

He next served two terms as a surgeon on a merchant vessel, plying between New York and Liverpool.

In December, 1855, Lane applied for a commission in the United States Navy. He was awarded his rank, placing first among all candidates. He impressed the Board by submitting, as part of the examination, an essay on " External Urethrotomy, written in Latin. In due course, Lane served on a navy ship that was stationed for a time off the coast of Central America. It was here that he performed a thyroidectomy on a Nicaraguan woman's goiter, an operation he had not performed before. It was a success and the patient recovered uneventfully.

Following his resignation from the navy, he spent over a year studying anatomy and clinical chemistry in Germany and France. This he did in order to prepare for the position of Professor of Physiology, offered to him by his uncle Elias Cooper, who had recently founded the first medical school in California(The Medical Department of the University of the Pacific).

Thus in July, 1861, L. C. Lane began his position on his uncle's medical school's staff. Due to his uncle's failing health, he was also forced to take on the editorship of the San Francisco Medical Press. At the death of his uncle in 1862, Lane helped to maintain the school, occupying the chair of anatomy. When the school was suspended in 1864, he was among those who joined the new Toland Faculty(the future UCSF).

In 1870, that same group, under the leadership of Dr. Lane, seceded from the Toland School and founded their own school. It was called the Medical Department of the University College. Lane had bigger plans for the school. In 1882, he renamed the school, the Cooper Medical School, in honor of his uncle. He then moved the school to a new brick building at Sacramento and Webster Streets, whose construction he had personally funded. As part of the move, he established an annual set of medical lectures for the public. He believed in educating the laity, even though the prevailing medical climate was "doctor knows best".

Following the construction of the medical school, two lots were added adjacent to the school. On this property Lane added two buildings. The first was a three story building. On the first floor was a large clinical lecture hall, on the second a large public lecture hall, and on the third was an anatomical amphitheater. The second building was the new Lane Hospital. This was staffed by the medical school staff but was open to all practitioners. A training school for nurses was also established at this hospital.

Dr. Lane was a prolific writer. He authored numerous papers on medical and surgical subjects. His painstakingly accurate and elegant styled articles are found in the local journals over a forty year period beginning in 1862. He had intended to combine some of the surgical articles into a three volume textbook on surgery but only the first volume, Surgery of the Head and Neck(1896) ever came to print.

The renowned Lane Medical Library was another of his visions. It became a reality after he and his wife had died. They had set aside sufficient funds in their respective wills for its construction and funding.

After a long and exhausting illness, death came to Dr. Lane on February 18, 1902. The nurse in attendance reported that "he suddenly awoke from a drowse, partially sat up and said, oh it is death, it is death" and then expired.

In 1908, Stanford University acquired Cooper Medical College as the nucleus for the Stanford Medical Department. The medical school and Lane Library were moved to the main campus in 1959.

Agnews State Hospital

By Michael A. Shea, MD

During the Gold Rush of 1849, psychiatric patients were locked up in ships (e.g. Ephemia) that had been abandoned in San Francisco Bay. Station houses (jails) were also used to confine these patients. By 1850, the San Francisco Marine Hospital was in use for the mentally ill. As California's population increased, the state authorized the first insane asylum to be constructed. It was built in Stockton in 1851. This was followed by Napa State Hospital in 1876.

Overcrowding at these two facilities led to the decision that a third hospital was needed. In 1855, the State purchased 323 acres of land from Abram Agnew, a seed farmer, located seven miles north of San Jose. Construction began in July 1866

Agnews State Hospital (1888 time period)

Agnews State Hospital (1966 time period)

and on October 30, 1888, 75 patients were transferred to this facility from Napa State Hospital. The name of the Agnew facility was The California Hospital for the Chronic Insane. The following year, the hospital's name changed to The State Insane Asylum at Agnews. (This was done in order that the hospital could accept acute, as well as chronic cases.) In 1897, the name changed, again, to Agnews State Hospital.

Architect Jacob Lenzen and son, Theodore, designed the first buildings on the site. The design was based on the Kirkbride Plan. This plan was named after Dr. Kirkbride, who wanted asylums to be conducive to the humane and moral treatment. The main building consisted of a four-story central administration section with two wings, each three stories high. In addition, a separate building housed a kitchen, bakery, laundry, carpenter shop, and a morgue. Grazing fields for dairy cattle, vegetable gardens, and fruit tree orchards filled the remaining 276 acres. Seven artesian wells supplied water for drinking and irrigation. Landscaping with shade and ornamental trees completed the project.

Treatment of patients mirrored the treatment in most parts of the country. Restraints, such as straight jackets, were used at times. Morphine, tonics, and stimulants were also employed as needed.

In 1890, Dr. F. W. Hatch (medical director) initiated a social program that involved live music and dancing. It was held every Friday evening with one-third of the patients allowed to attend. Guests were invited from surrounding towns. Although they were warned to be careful, Dr. Hatch told one visitor, "Do not offend the unfortunate persons you meet, and if they ask you to dance, do not refuse the request."

The inpatient population at Agnews continued to grow, and by 1906, there were over a hundred people employed and a total of 1,073 patients.

April 18, 1906, at 5:12 A.M., a 7.8 – 7.9 (moment magnitude scale) earthquake struck the San Francisco Bay Area. At Agnews, the majority of the buildings were destroyed and 117 staff and patients lost their lives.

Under the guidance of Dr. Leonard Stocking, hospital superintendent and medical director, the facility was rebuilt by 1911. It was done in the Mediterranean Revival style of tile roofs, decorative tile patterns, rustic wooden balconies, porch columns, and banisters. It was a layout resembling a college campus, consisting of two-story buildings and abundant lawns. The present clock tower building, however, copied closely the original administration and treatment building of 1888.

Agnews was a small self-contained town, including a multitude of construction trade "shops," a farm which raised pigs, chickens, and vegetable crops, a steam generating power plant for heating the buildings, a fire and police department, bakery, cannery, butcher shop, commissary, laundry, post office, and hospital.

Under Dr. Stocking's supervision, Agnews took on the characteristics of a progressive hospital as it was intended to be a "cheerful" place, with its decentralized buildings for different treatment purposes and different types of patients. He also instituted other programs for the inpatients such as civil war enactments, parades, camping excursions, and plays with patients as the actors.

In 1932, an expansion of Agnews resulted in a 424-acre East Campus known as the "colony." This would result in more buildings for patients and more land for farming.

In 1966, Agnews established the first program for individuals with developmental disabilities, consisting largely of mental retardation. The first patients consisted of 534 transfers from other facilities.

Due mainly to the emergence of neuro-pharmaceutical drug therapy, the 1971 Lanterman Act returned the mentally ill to the community or other facilities. In 1972, Agnews officially became The Agnews Developmental Center. Agnews now housed only patients with developmental disabilities. Activities and events such as Agnews Awareness Days encouraged interaction between patients and the general population. The rise of new values and programs that promoted individual growth and development, independence, and choices meant more patients could live in the community. In the mid 1990s, modern training sites were added on the smaller East Campus and the patients relocated to it. Agnews West Campus was declared surplus by the State in April 1996, and the 295-acre site was put up for sale. Community interest helped retain a 14-acre portion of the property that preserved the historic core.

In 1997, Sun Microsystems purchased 82.5 acres of the West Campus for its corporate headquarters and R&D campus. Sun agreed to restore four of the historic buildings (the auditorium, the clock tower, the superintendent's villa, and the administration building), some of which would be available for public use. Local historical groups worked with Sun to establish a history museum alongside the Historical Agnews Cemetery, where 300 former residents of Agnews are buried. Sun was acquired by the Oracle Corporation in 2010; the campus continues to be used as an Oracle R&D facility and conference center.

The Martinson Child Development Center and the Emergency Housing Consortium's Family Living Center occupy facilities on another portion of the Agnews property. The latter uses cottages that were moved from the former hospital complex. The Rivermark Planned Development Master Community stands on the remaining portion of the State surplus land. It consists of nearly 3,000 housing units, a library, shopping center, hotel, and other commercial and civic services.

The last developmentally disabled patient left the East Campus on March 26, 2009. Thus ended the 121-year history of Agnews State Hospital as a treatment center for the mentally ill and the developmentally disabled.

LEON PARRISH FOX, MD

Man Of The Century

By Michael A. Shea, MD

Preface

From a one-room schoolhouse in the hills of Kentucky to a residency program in obstetrics and gynecology at Santa Clara County Hospital, Leon P. Fox made the grade. After a four-and-a-half-year tour of duty in the Navy, serving as a medical officer on a troop transport ship in World War II, Leon began an illustrious career in the politics, practice, and education of medicine. He served as a delegate for the American Medical Association and the California Medical Association. He acted as a diplomat

and treasurer for a national medical organization, the American College of Obstetrics and Gynecology. He served as chief of staff at Santa Clara County Hospital (changed to Santa Clara Valley Medical Center in 1967), O'Connor Hospital, and San Jose Hospital. He helped found the Shufelt Gynecologic Society of Santa Clara Valley and became chairman and director of the ob/gyn residency program at the Santa Clara County Hospital from 1959 to 1970. He researched, wrote, and published 20 articles in his specialty. He practiced medicine in San Jose for over 30 years and delivered over 10,000 babies in his lifetime.

Elaborating on these remarkable achievements will form the major portion of the following biographical article. In conclusion, I would like to describe one of my favorite stories. It's about the man, rather than the doctor.

During the years 1970 to 1980, it was my privilege to assist Leon in many gynecological surgical cases at San Jose Hospital. Following each case, we would return to the physicians' locker room in order to change from scrub suits to street clothes. After the first few times, I noticed that Leon was always the first one to change and the first one out of the locker room. I decided to change this order and started racing back from surgery to dress as fast as I could. He was totally unaware of this little game. Flying through my combination lock, I would fling open the locker door. Scrubs would go flying in the general direction of the laundry bag while I grabbed for shirt, slacks, coat, and shoes. I changed as fast as I could, but the result was always the same. He continued to be first out the door. I never could catch him. I don't know many who could.

The Early Years

The ring of a phone will focus your attention like no other sound I know. This particular call happened in the spring of 1967. The voice of the caller was slow and deliberate, as he made me an offer I did not refuse. It was the position of first-year resident in the obstetric and gynecologic program at Santa Clara Valley Medical Center located in San Jose, California. The person making the offer was the chairman of the residency program, Dr. Leon Fox. The rest of this story is about the man on the other end of the phone, Leon Parrish Fox.

It began November 21, 1911. Leon was born to Milton and Hallie Fox in a small village named Trapp in the southeast section of Clark County, Kentucky. It is a rural area covered with nobs (low-lying hills) and thick groves of maple, poplar, and pine trees. It lies about 25 miles southeast of Lexington, Kentucky.

Leon was the oldest of five siblings. The other children were Elkin, born July 20, 1914; Marie and Milton junior (twins), born January 20, 1917; and Joyce, born April 17, 1933. The family lived in a house next door to their father's general store. They all had their turns in working at dad's store during their younger years. Local politicians frequented the store and many civic matters were decided by these men under the watchful eye of papa Milton. Leon's interest in politics, no doubt, had its origin here and contributed to his activities and achievements in later life.

Kindergarten through high school took place across the street from the Fox family home in a one-room schoolhouse. Leon, who was always known as the smart-but-quiet-one, was just three years of age when he started school and 16 years when he graduated. One incident in high school that stood out in Leon's memory was when he fell out of a swing and broke his arm. His father took him into town, which was about ten miles away, to see the local physician, Dr. Ishmael. He set the fracture and Leon's father became curious, asking a lot of questions. Dr. Ishmael got down the medical books and showed him how he treated the break. Then, they drove around the corner to the radiologist who took an x-ray and told them it looked real good. On the way home, his dad said, "You know, if I were you Leon, I'd be a doctor."[1]

Education

Taking his father's advice, he started his pre-med education in 1927 at Kentucky Wesleyan College. This was a methodist college in Winchester, Kentucky, which was close to home. A small pre-med society at school impressed Leon and nourished his growing interest in medicine. Since this was a two-year school, it was on to the University of Kentucky in Lexington to complete his undergraduate studies. He graduated in 1931 with a bachelor-of-arts degree. Medical school was the next step and it was to be the University of Louisville Medical School in Louisville, Kentucky. Graduation came in 1934 and plans for internship were already under way. Although Leon's mother wanted her boy to intern in Kentucky, the ultimate decision was Santa Clara County Hospital in San Jose, California. So in June of 1934, Leon and two of his fellow MDs, Jim Mayo and Bob Douds, fired up a 1929 Plymouth and made California- or-bust their motto. Each was going to a different location in California, where all became successful physicians.

June 26, 1934, Leon Fox walked in the door at Santa Clara Hospital, dressed in a white linen suit and white buck shoes. In true southern gentlemanly style, he asked the secretary who could help him with his bags? It did not take long for him to find out that interns handled their own bags and almost everything else in the hospital. Twenty dollars a month, meals, and laundry comprised the internship benefits. Interns in those days lived at the hospital and shared their quarters. Leon had three roommates: Jack Fogleman, Ezra Evans, and Jack Boden.

Six-week rotations through various divisions of medicine made up the year. These included: surgery, internal medicine, obstetrics, pediatrics, along with other subspecialties such as anesthesia, pathology, orthopedics, and tuberculosis. The latter was a large part of medical care and treatment in the 1930s and 1940s. A significant number of Dr. Fox's peers became infected with tuberculosis, although he himself never became ill.

Obstetrics and gynecology began to interest Leon at this time. He asked the chief of the county hospital, Dr. D. Wilson, if he could enter the residency program for OB/GYN at the hospital. Dr. Wilson told him he was too young to be an OB/GYN man. He said "go grow yourself a mustache, put on a pair of glasses, and if you can get Dr. Shufelt to take you for a year, I'll let you start your residency."[2] And that is exactly what he did.

Dr. A. Shufelt

Dr. Alson Anderson Shufelt, or "Shuey" as he was known as to most of his peers, was the first obstetrician gynecologist to establish a permanent practice in the Santa Clara Valley. He was born in Reno, Nevada on July 17, 1891. At age seven, his mother died in childbirth and he later resolved to be an OB/GYN and dedicate his life to improving the care of women in obstetrics. After living with his grandparents in Minnesota, he returned to Reno to rejoin his father who had remarried. He attended U.C. Berkeley for college and received an M.D. degree after four years at the University of California in San Francisco. His internship and OB/GYN residency were also at UCSF. In 1922, Dr. Shufelt began a solo practice at Sixth and Santa Clara Streets in San Jose. During his 28 years of practice, he acted as the first chairman of the obstetric department at county hospital, serving for several years and teaching many of the residents himself. He was known for his kindness and generosity of time, as many residents and patients attested to during those years. He was a meticulous surgeon who taught his students, including Leon, the lessons of careful anatomical dissection when performing hysterectomies and cesarean sections. He was always a credit to his profession, to his community, and a wonderful role model for young aspiring doctors.

Residency

Leon began a one year preceptorship with Dr. Shufelt in 1935 and developed much of his surgical skills under the guidance of Shuey. In 1936, mustache in place and preceptorship completed, Leon became the first OB/GYN resident at Santa Clara Hospital. He was given credit for the year with Dr. Shufelt, which allowed him to complete the residency in just two more years. Dr. Shufelt was one of his principle teachers along with Dr. Les Magoon, who would be a future associate of Leon's.

A residency program in obstetrics in 1936 would still be familiar to present day residents. The day would begin with hospital rounds, where both postpartum and post-operative patients would be seen by a team of doctors made up of an intern, resident, and, sometimes, an attending staff physician (a doctor in private practice who donated his time and expertise to teaching). The rest of the day would consist of surgery, seeing patients in outpatient clinic, educational seminars, deliveries, and, hopefully, lunch somewhere in-between. Night call generally came every third day and would routinely be interrupted by phone calls, emergency room visits, or deliveries. Endurance became a necessary quality in every resident and Leon developed more than his share.

In 1938, Leon received his certificate of completion in the OB/GYN residency program. He began private practice the same year in the St. Claire building in downtown San Jose. There were only three other doctors in that building at the time. They were Drs. Hal Williams, Tony Bonnani, and George Waters. Leon was the only OB/GYN physician among them.

Cleo

It was during the residency program that another very important person would come into Leon's life. Her name was Cleo Odem. She was the sixth child of Anderson and Nancy Odem. She was born October 1, 1917 in Sheridan, Oregon. Her mother died when she was a child and her older sister, Edna Mae, raised both Cleo and her sister Marjorie. The family lived and attended school in Oregon. Cleo went on to nursing school at St. Joseph's Hospital in San Francisco from 1934 to 1937. She and Leon met while Cleo was taking some of her training at the Santa Clara County Hospital. They fell in love and eloped to Reno, where they were wed on September 11, 1937. The marriage resulted in six children: two boys and four girls. All were born in San Jose.

World War II

December 7, 1941 resulted in a change of plans for nearly 80% of practicing physicians in San Jose. July 1942 found Dr. Fox in the medical corp of the United States Navy. He was commissioned as a full lieutenant. His assignment was the U.S.S. Humphreys (APD-12), a troop transport ship, designated to the Pacific Theater of Operations. It would function as a medical facility, bringing wounded soldiers from island invasion forces to hospital ships or land-based hospitals in the Pacific region. Capacity was 200 soldiers, one physician, and a small number of corp men. Their job was to take care of the wounded men and keep them stable until they could reach more advanced care facilities. The most traumatic experience recorded by Dr. Fox was having to amputate a young soldier's leg in order to save his life. The operation was successful.

There was occasional R&R for all aboard, when the ship would visit Brisbane, Australia. It was there that Leon was able to see his brother, Sgt. Milton B. Fox, who was in the Army. They were able to spend their first Christmas together in 12 years.

Thirty-six months of sea duty comprised most of Dr. Fox's active duty in the Navy. This included first wave participation in 12 invasions. Among these were the battles of Leyte, Luzon, Iwo Jima, and Okinawa. He received two letters of commendation for his naval service. After the war was over, Dr. Fox was promoted to lieutenant commander and transferred to Mare Island in San Pablo Bay, 25 miles northeast of San Francisco. The naval shipyard covered most of the island, where 1,598 ships were either repaired or built during World War II. Responsibilities for the lieutenant commander were mainly OB/GYN-related. January 1946 marked Leon's discharge from the service and his return to his family and private practice in San Jose.

The Shufelt Society

Shortly after reopening his practice at a new location on 14th and Santa Clara Streets in San Jose, Dr. Fox turned his attention to one of his passions, medical education. It was in 1946 that Dr. Fox founded the Shufelt Gynecologic Society of Santa Clara Valley. The name was chosen to honor Dr. Alson Shufelt, who acted as the society's first president. The organization consisted of local OB/GYN physicians who met monthly for dinner and an educational lecture given by speakers with expertise in their particular field of medicine. In addition, there was an annual two-day fall seminar sponsored by the society. It centered primarily on OB/GYN subjects with guest speakers from all across the United States. This local society became very successful largely because of the energy and enthusiasm for medical education that characterized Dr. Fox. He served as president from 1957 to 1959. The Shufelt Society endured for 59 years, with the last meeting held in 2005. Dr. Wakako Nomura, an OB/GYN physician at Kaiser Hospital in Santa Clara, was the last president.

County Residency

One of the most significant and respected accomplishments attributed to Dr. Fox was the OB/GYN residency program at the Santa Clara County Hospital. Although he was not the original chairman of the department, he assumed the chairmanship and directorship in 1959. Prior to that time, Dr. Shufelt, followed by Dr. James Muir, acted as chairman of the department. Under Dr. Fox's watch, 29 doctors received their OB/GYN certificates from 1959 to 1970. The three-year residency was fully accredited by the American College of OB/GYN and was considered one of the finest private programs in the country. Twenty-one out of the 29 graduated residents remained in the Santa Clara Valley for their practice. Encouraged by Dr. Fox, almost all of them became attending staff at the valley program, donating their time and talents in resident teaching. Leon cared deeply for his residents and always made certain there was adequate experience, diversity of pathology, and quality supervision in order for the graduate to be fully prepared for private practice.

Stanford Medical School assumed the program in 1970, and for the next seven years Stanford residents maintained the county residency. In 1977, the program again went private when Dr. Theodore Fainstat became chairman and director. Under his guidance and leadership, the residency remains to this day an example of quality medical education.

Dr. Fox was also somewhat of a pioneer when it came to women in medicine. He firmly believed they could participate on an equal basis with men in the obstetric and gynecologic field. This philosophy was in evidence when he encouraged and accepted Dr. Suzanne Regul into the residency program in 1965. She was the first female resident since the founding of the program and this was at a time when there were very few women in obstetrical residencies. He was also involved in nursing training by serving on the advisory boards of three nursing schools: San Jose City College, San Jose State University, and San Jose Hospital. Students rotated through his office on 15th Street, fulfilling part of their training requirements for office nursing duties and skills.

The Party

When the residency program at the county hospital passed to the Department of OB/GYN at Stanford University Medical School in 1970, it was a major changing of the guard. Before this actually took place, Dr. Fox felt so strongly about his attending staff that he ensured them all associate or assistant clinical instructor status with Stanford Medical School. He was watching out for his own.

As a result of the major change in the residency program, the county graduates decided to honor Leon with a dinner and award ceremony at Zorba the Greek, a local restaurant. Dr. Fred Schlichting was in charge of the festivities. The most vivid memory of the evening was when all the physicians watched a scantily-clad miss emerge from a giant three-tiered cake, followed by an apparent San Jose police officer proclaiming loudly that he was there to arrest the young lady for indecent exposure and the rest of the guests were to remain seated while names, addresses, and phone numbers were taken. Ten seconds of panic were eased when the prank was revealed by the perpetrator and master of ceremonies, Dr. Fred Schlichting. The remainder of the evening went without incident, but the occasion is still keenly remembered by all who were there.

National OB/GYN Societies

The American Board of Obstetrics and Gynecology was founded in 1930. Its purpose was to evaluate and certify those physicians who had completed an OB/GYN residency. This certification was accomplished by giving a written examination to a candidate during his residency and an oral examination two to three years into his practice. Dr. Fox completed his boards just after returning from the war.

The American College of Obstetrics and Gynecology (ACOG) had its origin on September 5, 1951. The purpose of this national organization was to establish and maintain the highest standards for OB/GYN care in educational and clinical practice. The organization also promoted research and publications in the field of obstetrics and gynecology. Leon was accepted as a Founding Fellow in ACOG in 1951. From 1969 to 1972, he served as vice-chairman of District VIII (west coast), and in 1976, he was elected treasurer of ACOG, which at the time represented more than 20,000 physicians across the United States. He held this position until 1982.

Leon published 20 papers from 1956 to 1985. They appeared in various medical journals such as the *American Journal of Obstetrics and Gynecology*, *Western Journal of Medicine*, *Trans Pacific Coast Obstetrical Gynecological Society*, and *California Medicine*. These papers were written about clinical disorders in OB/GYN. Each paper required many hours of research, reading, and writing before it would be presented to a journal for publication. He felt the work to prepare an article would increase his knowledge of the subject. It was a very effective method of continuing medical education.

Private Practice

In 1956, Leon and associate Les Magoon were joined in practice by Dr. Bert Johnson, fresh from his residency at Northwestern University in Chicago. He stayed for about two years and then moved over to the Good Samaritan Hospital area near Los Gatos. Bert would later serve as vice-chairman of the OB/GYN residency program at County Hospital. He was very active in teaching the residents, especially in gyn surgery. Dr. Merlin Johnson, following his discharge from the Navy, came on board in 1957 and remained with Dr. Fox until 1977, when he moved his practice to the Good Samaritan Hospital area.

Leon and Les Magoon built a new office building in 1958 at 303 North 15th Street. This location was just three blocks from San Jose Hospital. The convenience of this short distance was one of the reasons that inpatient care (deliveries and surgeries) was ultimately limited to San Jose Hospital. The only other hospital that he had used was O'Connor Hospital, which was several miles away. The new building had four physician offices, with two exam rooms for each doctor and two separate reception rooms. A fifth doctor's office and exam room were added later. Leon and Dr. Magoon occupied one half of the building and leased the other half to two independent doctors. The building was somewhat unique in that all exam rooms had their own adjoining bathrooms and change rooms. This is very seldom seen in today's medical offices.

Dr. Magoon retired in 1959 and it was not until 1970 that another physician joined Drs. Fox and Johnson. The third partner was Michael A. Shea, MD, who remained in practice at this location until 1980. Dr. Shea was in the last group of three residents to graduate from the Valley Medical Center while Dr. Fox was in charge of the program. The other two were Robert C. Allin, MD, who practiced in Honolulu, Hawaii, and David L. Garrison MD, who practiced in St. Joseph, Missouri.

Private practice for Dr. Fox was very successful and busy. When asked, after his retirement, how many babies he had delivered in his career, his answer was about 10,000. He could have been even more specific, as he had written down all the names and dates of every mother he had delivered, even in his training years. Queried about his most challenging cases, he recalls two. The first was a lady with twins who had severe polyhydramnios (excess fluid in the sac around the baby). She went into labor and, because of the large amount of fluid in the uterus, she started having heart failure. He placed a plastic catheter into the sac and drained off eight gallons of fluid. The mother survived, but the premature twins who were very small did not live. The second case Dr. Fox remembered vividly was one referred to him by a local OB physician. The patient was a hospital nurse having her first baby. She was in active labor, but the baby was in a breech position. When Dr. Fox arrived, the baby's trunk was delivered, but the head was locked in the birth canal. After much difficulty, the delivery was completed, but the infant did suffer spinal cord injuries with residual defects. These cases stood out in Dr. Fox's mind not only because of the complications, but because of the outcomes. However, there were hundreds and hundreds of other complicated pregnancies where, because of his knowledge and skill, good outcomes were the result. He had a large referral source from many of the family practitioners in the area. Even other obstetricians would ask for consultation for their more difficult cases. He was also known as a very accomplished gyn surgeon. He paid particular attention to anatomical details in his abdominal and vaginal hysterectomies. This attention to details no doubt began with his preceptorship with Dr. Shufelt.

Although hard work was his trademark, Dr. Fox always reserved two weeks in July for a vacation. One of his favorite destinations was a cabin near Vida, Oregon. There, he enjoyed fly-fishing on the McKenzie River. It was there that Leon and his family could spend quiet days together, away from the pressures and time constraints of private practice.

Organization Memberships

The following list of medical and civic affiliations, with positions held, is presented here in order to appreciate what incredible accomplishments he achieved during his lifetime. These are even more remarkable when viewed in the context of a large private practice.

Hospitals

- O'Connor Hospital: Active 1938 to 1970; Chief of Staff 1946 to 1948
- San Jose Hospital: Active 1938 to 1985; Chief of Staff 1960
- Santa Clara Valley Medical Center: Active 1938 to 1985; Chief of Staff 1953 to 1956

Professional Organizations

- Santa Clara County Medical Society - 1937 to 1985
  President 1957
- California Medical Association - 1937 to 1985
  Delegate 1946
- American Medical Association - 1937 to 1985, Delegate 1966
- American Association for Maternal and Child Health, President 1972
- California Association for Maternal and Child Health, President 1971
- American College of Surgeons , Fellow 1941
- Shufelt Gynecological Society of Santa Clara Valley Founder 1946; President 1957 to 1959
- Peninsula Gynecological Society, President 1954
- American College of Obstetrics and Gynecology
  Founding Fellow 1957
  District VIII, Vice Chairman 1969 to 1972
  District VIII, Representative to the committee on nominations 1971 to 1972
  Committee on Health Care Delivery 1973 to 1976
  Treasurer 1976 to 1982
- Pacific Coast OB/GYN Society - 1956 to 1985; President 1980 to 1981
- San Francisco Gyn Society - 1956 to 1985; President 1966 to 1967
- American Board of OB/GYN Diplomat 1948
- Santa Clara County Tuberculosis Association
- Santa Clara County Chapter of American Cancer Society, President 1961
- Santa Clara County Chapter of American Heart Society, President 1956
- San Jose Chapter American Red Cross Blood Bank, Director 1948
- New York Academy of Sciences - 1964
- Public Health League of California, Councilor 1964 to 1970
- California Political Medical Action Committee Director 1968 to 1972
- Institute for Medical Research Vice President 1976

Civic

- City of San Jose Advisory Board of Health - 1946 to 1951
- San Jose Rotary Club - 1941 to 1985
- San Francisco Common Wealth Club
- Boys City Boys Club; Director 1958; President 1965
- Calvary Methodist Church Board of Trustees
- San Jose City College of Nursing; Advisory Board

- San Jose State University of Nursing; Advisory Board
- San Jose Hospital of Nursing; Advisory Board

The aforementioned position of chief of staff at the three hospitals is no ordinary task. It is the highest elected position for a physician in a governing role at a given hospital. The chief of staff is responsible for verifying credentials of applicants to the hospital medical staff, ensuring quality of care for patients, initiating any disciplinary actions that may be necessary, and carrying out all the other rules and regulations that apply to the medical staff. He conducts monthly executive council meetings made up of all the various department chairmen. Quarterly meetings of the entire physician membership of the hospital are also the responsibility of the chief of staff. These duties required many hours away from the office and were all done gratuitously.

Little Learners

One of the organizations is not on the above list, but needs recognition, as it was one of Dr. Fox's favorites. It was called the Little Learners. This home-based club was formed in 1933 by ten San Jose physicians of varying specialties. When Leon joined in 1938, there were 30 members. This eclectic group would meet monthly at one of the members' homes and the medical subject would be presented by one of the members. Food and drink were also enjoyed by all. In 1985, Leon hosted, what was to be, his last Little Learners meeting. One participant remembers Leon opening a special thirty-year-old bottle of Chateau Lafite Rothschild, saying that this was a special wine for a special time. Dr. Donald Threlfall, one of the original founders, penned a memorable editorial in the 1972 book on the history of the Little Learners. He may well have had Leon in mind when he wrote, "it fascinates me to rub shoulders and be associated with men who are so respected on so many levels: not just county, but state, national and world, all from this little group."[3]

Man of the Century

A man of the century award only comes along every 100 years or so. On May 14, 1976, this unusual honor was conferred upon Leon Fox by the Santa Clara Valley Medical Center on its centennial anniversary celebration. The event was held at the San Jose Hyatt House and included in the 250 attendees were all the former residents who had graduated from the OB/GYN residency program under Dr. Fox. Cited as some of the reasons for the award were his 40 years of dedicated service to that hospital, his OB/GYN chairmanship from 1959 to 1970, and his being chief of staff from 1953 to 1956. The selection was a carefully kept secret and it did surprise Dr. Fox. Upon receipt of the plaque, he remarked that it left him speechless, added a thank you, and promptly sat down. This was typical Leon Fox. The man who had done so much for his patients and peers throughout his lifetime would rarely talk about himself.

The Final Days

In December of 1984, Dr. Fox began to experience some worrisome symptoms, suggesting a possible brain tumor. A CT scan confirmed a lesion in the brain and a needle biopsy revealed cancer. Surgery was ruled out and he was treated with external radiation and chemotherapy. The prognosis was not good, but he continued to work in the office during 1985. He passed away quietly April 29, 1986 in his home on South 16th Street, where he had lived for 39 years. The most poignant and meaningful memorial came from the physicians, nurses, and staff of the Obstetric Department at Valley Medical Center. It is a fitting tribute to the man and his life.

"Dr. Fox generously gave of his knowledge, skills, and services throughout his lifetime. We will dearly miss his presence, but we all have a bit of his wisdom to cherish and keep forever."[4]

End Notes

1. "Oral interview: Leon P. Fox MD," Santa Clara County Medical Association, 3 Nov. 1985:1
2. "Oral interview: Leon P. Fox MD." 13
3. "Donald R. Threlfall, The Little Learners (San Jose: Santa Clara County Medical Society, 1973) 14
4. "Leon P. Fox, S.J. Physician, "San Jose Mercury News 1 May 1986: 8

Bibliography

Arbuckle, Clyde. "Clyde Arbuckle's History of San Jose."San Jose: Smith and McKay, 1985.

Bruntz, George. "History of Los Gatos-Gem of the Foothills".Valley Publishers, 1971.

"Cory Name Tied To Early Medic". San Jose News 11 August 1972.

"County of Santa Clara Invoices" 1850-1884 Signposts Page 39.

Garcia, Lorie. "Agnews Asylum, Hospital, Development Center 1885-1996" Santa Clara: Lorie Garcia, 2003.

"Gardens of the World of Santa Clara County." California: The Lewis publishing Company. 1888.

Goodman and Gilman. "The Pharmaceutical Basis of Therapeutics." New York: The Macmillan Company, 1960.

Harris MD, Henry. "California's Medical Story." Baltimore: Charles C. Thomas, 1932.

Heizer, Robert F. "The Castanoan Indians" Mountain View: W.B. Associates, 1974.

Hruby, Daniel D."Mines to Medicine" San Jose: O'connor Hospital. 1965.

Jackson. "Indians, Franciscan, and Spanish Colonization" 1995.

Larsell, O. "The Doctor in Oregon" Portland: Binfords and Mort, 1947

Lyman, George D. "Beginning of California Medical History." California Western Medicine: May 1925.

Lyman, George D. John Marsh Pioneer, New York, 1933.

Lyon, Marylou."Some More Pioneer Women of Santa Clara County California" Cupertino: Grandma Lyon Enterprises,1999.

Margolin, Malcolm. "The Ohlone Way". Berkeley: Heyday Books, 1978.

McKevill." The University of Santa Clara, a History 1851-1977" Stanford Press, 1979.

Pryor, Alton. "Little Known Tails in California History". Roseville: Stagecoach Publishing, 1997.

"Reflections of the Past-An Anthology of San Jose." Heritage Media Corporation. 1996.

Reid, Marjorie. "Ascension Solorsand." Cupertino: Deanza College Student Research Paper, 1992.

Rothstein, William G. "American Physicians in the Nineteenth Century" Baltimore: The Johns Hopkins University Press, 1972.

Sandoz. "Converting California: 2004".

"San Jose and Esmeralda" San Jose Mercury News. 30 June 1903 Page 102.

"San Jose Common Council Meeting Minutes" 4-13-1850 to 1-6-1851.

San Jose Historical Museum Association. "Sunshine Fruit and Flowers" San Jose: San Jose Mercury Publishing Company. 1987.

Sawyer, Eugene T . "History of Santa Clara County California." Los Angeles: Historic Record Company, 1922.

Shryock, Richard Harrison. "Medicine in America." Baltimore: The Johns Hopkins Press, 1966.

Skowronek "Telling the Santa Clara Story" Santa Clara University 2002.

Speert, Harold. "Obstetrics and Gynecology in America A History." Baltimore: Waverly Press Inc., 1980.

Steele, Volney, "Bleed, Blister, and Purge." Mountain Press Publishing 2005.

"The Castonoan Indians" Mountain View: W.B. Associates, 1974.

Vision and Progress. "A Commemorative History of San Jose Hospital" Editorial Consultants Inc. 1983.

Webb, Edith Buckland. "Indian Life at the Old Missions." Los Angeles: Warren F. Lewis. 1952.

Weber. Encyclopedia of California Catholic Heritage. 2000.

"When San Jose was Young" San Jose Evening News-a series of articles 1916 to 1934.

Yasin. "The Roots of Healing" Research Manuscript Series. Santa Clara University 1995.